EXPLORING EMOTIONAL HEALTH

kevin mayhew

kevin
mayhew

First published in Great Britain in 2017 by Kevin Mayhew Ltd
Buxhall, Stowmarket, Suffolk IP14 3BW
Tel: +44 (0) 1449 737978 Fax: +44 (0) 1449 737834
E-mail: info@kevinmayhew.com

www.kevinmayhew.com

© Copyright 2017 Liz Edge

The right of Liz Edge to be identified as the author of this work has been asserted
by her in accordance with the Copyright, Designs and Patents Act 1988.

The publishers wish to thank all those who have given their permission to
reproduce copyright material in this publication.

Every effort has been made to trace the owners of copyright material and
we hope that no copyright has been infringed. Pardon is sought and apology
made if the contrary be the case, and a correction will be made in any
reprint of this book.

All rights reserved. No part of this publication may be reproduced, stored in
a retrieval system, or transmitted, in any form or by any means, electronic,
mechanical, photocopying, recording, or otherwise, without the prior written
permission of the publisher.

Scripture quotations are taken from *The Holy Bible, New International Version®*,
NIV® Copyright © 1973, 1978, 1984, 2011 by Biblica, Inc.®

Used by permission. All rights reserved worldwide.

9 8 7 6 5 4 3 2 1 0

ISBN 978 1 84867 913 9
Catalogue No. 1501551

Cover design by Justin Minns
© Image used under licence from Shutterstock Inc.
Edited by Virginia Rounding
Typeset by Angela Selfe

Printed and bound in Great Britain

Contents

About the author

Liz Edge is a professionally qualified Youth Work Practitioner with a First-Class BA (Hons) Degree in Youth Work and Ministry. She has contributed to the work of local and national organisations, most recently including *Romance Academy, selfharmUK* and *Premier Youth and Children's Work*.

As a freelancer, Liz is able to offer a wide range of innovative youth work through education, training and intervention. Her practice is made authentic by drawing from her own life's adversities, which includes living with depression and anxiety for over a decade.

In all her pioneering work, Liz's ethos is to provide holistic support to adolescents in their relationships and to promote positive well-being: with themselves, with others and with the wider world.

When not in youth work mode, you can usually find Liz drinking coffee in her home town of Ashley Cross or relaxing on Bournemouth beach with her husband, Nick.

Foreword by Ali Campbell

Exploring Emotional Health is a fantastic blend of wisdom, vital information and sensitively structured workshop sessions for young people. Youth leaders, who might be wary or unsure about tackling topics like anxiety and depression, are gently led through some introductory sessions about identifying and coping with emotions – myths are debunked, stereotypes are challenged and your confidence in tackling this subject will grow.

What is a bonus, and sets this resource book apart from many others, is the holistic way that Liz approaches the whole subject and each section. It is so important to be a reflective practitioner, but what is rare is to see questions for the youth workers to ask of themselves, as well as their young people. This might be a tool for a youth group – and, in fact, you could draw on different elements in numerous work contexts – but it is also a tool for the youth leader. In work and ministry, one of the best things we can offer young people is a 'healthy us'. That doesn't mean we are emotionally 'sorted', but it does mean we are prepared to go on a journey and explore our own emotions, as well as those of our young people, and become more emotionally literate ourselves.

This book is a gift to the Church and a gift to youth work. If you want to see young people live life to the full (and 'full' means our whole selves, everything we are, including our emotions), then I encourage you to get it.

Ali Campbell
Youth and Children's Ministry Consultant
www.theresource.org.uk

Introduction

Exploring Emotional Health: Six workshop outlines for youth leaders is a practical resource for youth leaders tackling some of the most common mental and emotional health challenges young people face today. How can I be a Christian and be diagnosed with depression? If the Bible tells me to not worry, then why am I so anxious all the time? Does God still love me, even though I self-harm?

These challenges raise important questions about the spirituality of adolescence. Very few resources exist that address these questions in a youth-friendly way; *Exploring Emotional Health* begins to meet that need.

Each chapter provides core information around a given topic as well as ready-to-go practical workshops to enable even the busiest of youth leaders to provide effective support in building resilient young people.

Every workshop is the start of an ongoing conversation. It's about embracing the uncomfortable, mixing the mid-week more formal Bible study with the topics discussed at the informal Friday night drop-in. It's about supporting youth leaders in reflective practices to grow and become knowledgeable themselves, just as much as the young people.

Written for youth leaders, its user-friendly nature and topical relevance opens this book to all those who have a connection with young people. It can be used as a tool to support youth leaders as they educate volunteers; for teachers seeking an alternative lesson plan to the well experienced youth leader needing a 'refresher'.

Youth leaders are encouraged to use their initiative when it comes to timings and group sizes. The workshops can be used as a series or for one-off events. Every youth group is different; therefore, the workshops will be unique for everyone. The possibilities for the use of this book are endless.

The flow of the book

It begins with a brief introduction to safeguarding and professional practice which can refresh existing knowledge. It is vital to be competent in this area, due to the sensitive nature of the topics explored in this book.

Chapters follow a similar format to aid accessibility and conceptual flow. Each chapter begins with a clear definition of the topic, with an exploration of signs and symptoms, treatment options and key facts. There follows a suggestion of a biblical narrative that connects to the topics. How the given topic relates to adolescents' lives and their experiences is weaved throughout, followed by a reflective moment specifically for the reader. Each chapter concludes with an annotated workshop plan, offering practical notes on how to run the session effectively.

An appendix and further reading suggestions conclude the book. All six workshops can be found in the appendix without any annotations, so that they can be photocopied for convenience.

Safeguarding and professional practice
Safeguarding is everyone's responsibility

Everyone who works with children – defined as anyone under the age of 18 years – has a responsibility for keeping them safe. No single professional can have a full picture of a child's needs and circumstances. Therefore, everyone who comes into contact with children has a role to play in identifying concerns, sharing information correctly and taking prompt action. Any professional who has concerns about a child's welfare should make a referral to the local authority's children's social care.

A child-centred approach

For safeguarding to be effective, it must be child-centred. Keep the needs and views of the children at the centre and do not place the interests of adults ahead of the needs of the child. Anyone working with children should be guided by the following principles:

- see and speak to the child

- listen to what they say

- take their views seriously

- work with them collaboratively when deciding how to support their needs.[1]

How to safeguard yourself as a worker and your work place when discussing mental and emotional health

Everyone's workplace should have a safeguarding and child protection policy to which all workers adhere. These should be live documents that are on display and easily accessed rather than hidden away in an office.

As a youth leader, it's crucial that you familiarise yourself with these documents on a regular basis, knowing what to do if you or any volunteers who work with you have any concerns. Don't forget to check whether policies need updating or copies need to be given to volunteers.

Safeguarding should not be a hidden topic from young people. Instead, they too should be aware of what steps should be taken when they share a concern and of the wider support available.

Safeguarding should be a topic that you discuss during supervision, updating your supervisor on any concerns you have and vice versa. This is a space where your supervisor should check up on how you are safeguarding yourself and whether you need to step back from any cases.

Supporting young people can become emotionally draining, so safeguard your time and use appropriate spaces – like supervision – to look after yourself. We must be healthy workers if we are to support adolescents effectively.

How to safeguard young people when running the workshops

Where possible, it is helpful to be aware of any challenges linked to the workshops that a young person may already be facing. This will help safeguard the young people.

---

1. HM Government (2015) *Working together to safeguard children*. Available at: https://www.gov.uk/government/publications/working-together-to-safeguard-children--2 [Accessed: 16 February]

For example, if you are going to run the self-harm workshop, take a moment to think whether it could trigger something for any of the young people in your group. It may be appropriate to have a conversation with them prior to the workshop, so they are aware of what they are attending.

Make young people aware of your safeguarding process, not forgetting to explain that it is there to support them. Let them know where to go for additional support if they need it.

During the workshops, be aware of the young people's behaviours. Have any of them become particularly quiet when they are usually a loud member? Have any of them become particularly tearful? Observe their body language and make them aware that they can take a moment outside the workshop to compose themselves if they need to. Try and defuse any unhelpful emotional outbursts, reminding the group that you're exploring these topics because they are mature enough to talk about them, and because these are important topics to discuss.

How to know when a higher level of support is needed for a young person

It is vital that you report any concerns you have to your workplace's safeguarding officer, and then to your local authority if necessary. Don't keep safeguarding issues just within your workplace; your information could be the final piece of the jigsaw for action to be taken to support a young person.

Be intuitive and use your youth leader wisdom to assess the situation. Do you feel out of your depth in supporting that young person? Have you tried appropriate intervention but it hasn't worked? Have your concerns built up over time? If in doubt, talk to your supervisor and safeguarding officer to find out what to do next.

You have the power to report any concerns to the local authority – do so, if you feel the correct action hasn't been taken by your workplace.

Be smart – if you think a young person is in immediate danger to themselves or others, call 999 and report it to the police.

ONE

Identifying emotions

Identifying emotions is a key part in developing a person's emotional intelligence – the ability to recognise, understand and manage our own emotions.[2] Developing these skills is a life-long process and fundamental to living an enriching life.

It can sometimes be difficult to identify the specific emotions we're experiencing, or even correctly determine the reason why we're feeling that way. They can be complex and at any given moment a person may experience multiple, even contradictory, emotions.

Sometimes our feelings can 'hide' behind other feelings which can further complicate our understanding. For example, a person may think they are angry and display that by shouting, but they may actually be feeling very hurt. Yet being able to identify emotions – in oneself and others – is vital in supporting our mental health.

If we became more emotionally healthy people, we could:

- recognise signs of poor mental health in ourselves and others
- identify when additional support is needed and have the confidence to ask for help
- build healthy relationships with ourselves, others and the wider world

Setting the scene

The need for better understanding around a person's emotional wellbeing is greater than ever, especially in childhood and during adolescence. Here's a picture of the scene we're facing:

---

2. D. Goleman (1996), *Emotional Intelligence*, London: Bloomsbury.

One in ten children and young people aged five to sixteen suffer from a diagnosable mental health disorder. That's around three students in every class.[3]

Have you recently taught a lesson in your local high school? Ever thought that up to three of those students could be suffering from a diagnosable mental health disorder?

More than half of all adults with mental health problems were diagnosed in childhood. Less than half were treated appropriately at the time.[4]

Tackling the problem at a young age gives that person the chance to grow into a healthy adult. Youth leaders can be part of a network of provision for a young person who has a mental health diagnosis, supporting them appropriately as they grow into adulthood.

72% of children in care have behavioural or emotional problems – these are some of the most vulnerable people in our society.[5]

This is a huge percentage and, most likely, the actual percentage is even higher. Do you work with children in care? How are you supporting some of these most vulnerable people?

Statistics can be helpful to see the wider picture, but it is key to remember that every youth leader is in a different context. Yet all youth leaders have the power to some degree of supporting the emotional development of the adolescents they encounter.

Jesus' emotions

Often, we come to our faith from an intellectual stance, engaging in theological conversation and literature, often ignoring – consciously or unconsciously – the emotion behind what is being read. Our emotional maturity is not always given the same degree of respect as a person's academic knowledge. When it comes to our spirituality, our emotions can be viewed as leading us astray or as being immature.

3. H. Green, A. McGinnity, H. Meltzer et al (2005), *Mental health of children and young people in Great Britain 2004*, London: Palgrave.
4. J. Kim-Cohen, A. Caspi, T.E. Moffitt et al (2003), 'Prior juvenile diagnoses in adults with mental disorder', *Archives of General Psychiatry* 60: 709-717.
5. J. Sempik et al (2008), 'Emotional and behavioural difficulties of children and young people at entry into care' *Clinical Child Psychology and Psychiatry* 13 (2): 221-233.

There is definitely a wider conversation that needs to take place about our spirituality and emotions, especially with adolescents who are at a particularly vulnerable place in their development of identity in the world. We also cannot ignore that Jesus had emotions – a man of sorrows and of joy.

When it comes to teaching young people about the gospel, it is vital that we approach it from a holistic point of view, and that includes the emotions Jesus, and others in the Bible, experienced.

Further information

There are two key books which are commonly used in learning more about emotional intelligence and literacy. These are:

- Daniel Goleman, *Emotional Intelligence,* Bloomsbury, 1996.

- Claude Steiner, *Emotional Literacy: Intelligence with a Heart,* Personhood Press, 2003.

The Revd Dr Jeremy Thomson provides a theological insight into relationships and emotions in his book:

- Jeremy Thomson, *Relationships and Emotions after Christendom,* Paternoster Press, 2016.

Pause for thought

It might be helpful to find a quiet space, away from your usual environments and ponder the following questions.

- Using the scale of 1 (not at all) to 5 (extremely important), how important are emotions to you in your life? Are they a main feature or an 'added extra' to who you are?

- How would you describe your ability to recognise how others are feeling? Does this factor into your relationships with others?

- Thinking of your relationship with God, how often do you share how you honestly feel with him?

- Reflecting on yourself as a young person, how in touch were you with your emotions? Were you raised to see emotions as a strength, or perhaps as a weakness?

It may be that this moment has caused several other thoughts or feelings to arise. Make sure to look after yourself and perhaps discuss them with a person you trust.

Workshop

This workshop is very much the start of highlighting the need for emotional intelligence and literacy with ourselves and our faith. It is about supporting young people to critically engage with their emotional development – wherever they are at. To some it may seem simple but to others it is much harder to understand that our emotions – and those of Jesus – go far beyond happy and sad.

Moving forward

One way of moving forward with this workshop is to include it in your future Bible studies, focusing on the emotions that are going on in the passage as well on as the action that is being taken.

Identifying emotions

(Annotated Workshop Outline)

Resources Needed
- Whiteboard/flipchart paper
- Pens
- Prizes
- Advice scenarios
- Bibles

Aim:

To understand why feelings are important and to identify the emotions of others and ourselves.

Leader's Notes:

So often when we discuss emotions and feelings there is a negative connotation to it, as if it is a sign of weakness. This is an opportunity to debunk this myth and show how Jesus had emotions too!

Don't be put off if your youth group aren't ecstatic at the idea of talking about emotions. This is all part of changing the culture many young people live in where emotions are considered feeble, or it's only girls that get to express their feelings. Debunk the gender stereotype and be a part of this change!

Emotional charades

DO: First, ask for a volunteer to be the scribe. Then ask the rest of the group to shout out all the emotions they can think of and ask the scribe to write them down.

Encourage the group to be more creative in their thinking of emotions than just 'happy' and 'sad'. What emotions have they felt this week?

Tired? Thankful? Anxious? Hopeful? Guilty? Joyful? Angry? Cheerful? Rejected? Loved? Overwhelmed? Hateful? Daring? Insecure? There are *so* many emotions that we can feel, so get them thinking!

After a good number of emotions have been written down, split the group into two teams. Ask for a volunteer from each team to come to the front. Secretly give them an emotion from the board. They then act it out to their teams, and the first team to guess it correctly wins a point. This can be done for as long as time allows – perhaps even have a prize ready for the winning team!

This is an opportunity to encourage laughter, let those who love acting embrace their theatrical skills, and move our thoughts beyond happy and sad.

Jesus' emotions

SAY: Jesus' emotions played a huge feature in his existence on earth. As we study his life, we discover so many scenarios where he experienced a whole heap of feelings – from being a man of sorrows to a man of joy!

ASK: Take a moment to ask the group if they can think of any examples of where Jesus felt and expressed his emotions in the Bible.

Here are some examples that could help this discussion. You could even split them up, asking small groups to discuss and identify the emotions.

It may be helpful to find your own biblical examples. Have you recently been studying a particular Bible story that you could use? Try and utilise the work you have already done with the group, rather than adding new examples which could be confusing. Remember, these examples all have a context, so make sure they are explained if the group find them confusing at all.

Jesus is tested in the wilderness (Matthew 4)

An example here is when Jesus said: 'Away from me, Satan!' (v.10) and the devil left. I doubt Jesus said it in a quiet, timid voice but with a powerful tone, showing just how much he wants and believes in honouring the Lord our God.

The guards mock Jesus (Luke 22:63-65)
When the guards mocked Jesus, how do you think that affected how he felt? Maybe he felt rejected and lonely.

Gethsemane (Mark 14)
When Jesus said: 'My soul is overwhelmed with sorrow to the point of death' (v.34), it is highly unlikely that he was feeling cheerful. How does an overwhelmed soul feel?

You could add to this by asking if anyone has any examples of when they could tell a friend was upset and they offered to help them. What body language did their friend display? Did they say they were upset or could you just tell; if so, why?

SAY: It's important we take note of our feelings rather than ignoring them, as they are a part of who God created us to be. Our emotions can help us grow our sense of self-worth and can help guide us through life. Emotions are so powerful that they can help us know when to support a friend who's upset, or know when to walk away from an argument. Jesus had feelings; if we are on a quest to become more Christ-like beings, then it's time to learn more about them!

Advice time
By offering advice to others, using our Christ-like nature, the group will be able to look outside themselves and begin to identify emotions of others and subsequently themselves. Feel free to create your own scenarios.

Offering advice to others is a great technique in helping young people discuss topics that they themselves may find difficult to approach. It removes them directly from the scenario but offers great insight into their thoughts and how they would react if it was them.

SAY: We all come across various friends and family members who sometimes need advice – including ourselves! Jesus was amazing at giving advice to others and now it's time for us to offer the advice. In pairs/small groups, pick a scenario and discuss the questions at the end. Be ready to explain it to the rest of the group afterwards.

It might be helpful to ask the group to act out the scenarios, bringing them to life! This is an opportunity to encourage confidence in the young people in their ability to support others, building their self-esteem. It's also a chance to learn more about the young people and the differences in opinions. Encourage the group to try and get through all the questions so they have a wider scope of advice for the scenario, ready to feedback to the rest of the group.

Scenario 1 – Nick and Jamie

For Nick's twelfth birthday his parents took him and a friend to Marwell zoo for the day. He was looking forward to seeing the penguins because they were his favourite! Nick's friend, Jamie, wanted to spend most of his time at the monkey enclosure. The weather changed and the heavy rain meant they all had to go inside. They waited for the rain to stop but it didn't, so Nick's parents decided to take them all home early, without seeing the penguins.

- How do you think Nick might have felt throughout the day?
- Did his feelings change as the day went on? If so, how?
- How do you think Jamie might have felt?
- Did his feelings change throughout the day? If so, how?
- Looking back, how do you think Nick will remember his birthday celebration?

Scenario 2 – Sarah and Gemma

Sarah and Gemma took the bus into town to go shopping. Their parents gave each of them money to pay for the bus tickets. On the way into town, Gemma paid for both of their bus tickets. After they had finished shopping, they decided to get the bus back home. However, Sarah had spent all of the money she took with her, including the bus ticket money from her parents. They were stuck in town alone.

- How do you think Sarah might have felt throughout the day?
- Did her feelings change as the day went on? If so, how?
- How do you think Gemma might have felt?
- Did her feelings change throughout the day? If so, how?
- What memories do you think they will have of this shopping trip?

Scenario 3 – Bethany and Sam

Bethany and Sam have been best friends since primary school. For Bethany's birthday, she went to Thorpe Park and took Sam with her. Sam told Bethany he was scared of the rollercoasters but wanted to go on them. Bethany encouraged Sam to go on one, promising that she'd sit next to him. Sam was so thrilled he conquered his fear and they both enjoyed their day.

- How do you think Bethany might have felt throughout the day?
- Did her feelings change as the day went on? If so, how?
- How do you think Sam might have felt?
- Did his feelings change throughout the day? If so, how?
- What memories do you think they will have of Bethany's birthday celebration?

DO: Take some time to ask each pair/group to feedback their thoughts on the scenario(s). Can they relate to any of them? Does anyone have their own real-life scenario to share?

Close

Take a moment to pray for the group, asking our heavenly Father to help us all realise the power of feelings and remember that acknowledging them is a strength and not a weakness. Perhaps ask one of the group members if they would like to pray for you all.

Challenge

SAY: Over the next week I challenge you to try and identify your emotions and see if they match some of the emotions we have explored today. When you're reading your Bible, think 'is there an emotion I can identify here?' and bring it back next week!

TWO

Coping with emotions

Managing emotions is another important part in a person's emotional intelligence. It's about knowing how to cope with the emotions we experience in a healthy manner. It is a learning process that begins in infancy and grows throughout a person's life.

Emotions can be extremely powerful and learning how to manage them is key to becoming emotionally healthy beings. Coping with emotions is the next step to take after identifying the emotions people experience.

It's important to be able to recognise if we are managing our emotions well or letting our emotions manage us. By not having the coping skills, there can be a negative effect on a person's life in all areas – work, school, social commitments, relationships, to name a few.

Communication

Communication is key in supporting the emotional and mental health of all people. Equipping adolescents to communicate how they are feeling and providing a safe space to learn how to cope when those feelings become overwhelming will help them to develop their emotional health. They will have the skills to be able to communicate with others when they need a little extra support and also have the ability to begin to recognise if higher levels of support are needed.

What are the signs of someone struggling to cope with their emotions?

There is no set list, but here are some signs to look out for which could mean a person isn't managing their emotions in a healthy manner.

- Unable to articulate what emotion(s) they are experiencing
- Becomes easily frustrated by situations and/or people
- Regularly experiencing anxiety
- Unable to recognise the cause of the emotion they are experiencing
- Only displaying emotions to the extremes
- Indulging in risky behaviours
- Engaging in excessive alcohol/drug misuse.

Vulnerable adolescents

It's important that as a person grows they have a safe space where they can express their emotions and learn to cope with them. For some, this is a lot more difficult than for others. Adolescents who are particularly vulnerable to not learning coping skills include:

- Children in care
- Those whose parents are separating/divorcing
- Those with long-term health conditions
- Those with disabilities
- Victims of abuse.

Youth leaders are in a great position to model how to manage emotions, especially to some of the most vulnerable young people in society. A dysfunctional youth group could be a tell-tale sign that some young people are struggling without necessarily coming to you and asking for support. A healthy youth group is an excellent space for vulnerable adolescents in which to learn coping skills and generally explore their emotional health.

Emotional health in faith

Our emotional health is not an isolated part of who we are. It can be weaved throughout our beliefs and actions, affecting us as whole beings from physical to spiritual. When it comes to faith, our emotions are often dismissed as an unreliable source, yet this doesn't have to be the case.

Just like saying to ourselves that it is not physically healthy to eat a tub of ice cream every day even though we may feel it will help pick us up, the same can be translated into our spiritual relationship. We may feel that God is not responding to our prayers, but instead of getting angry at God or feeling let down as our emotions are telling us, we trust that God knows what he is doing. Taking leaps of faith at times can build up our confidence in managing our emotions, knowing that God is in control. It doesn't have to be a one player game, as we can rely on his strength to carry us forward. It's about finding a helpful balance that acknowledges our feelings but also takes into consideration our common sense and overall health.

Further information

There is a lot of support and education that can teach people of all ages about the importance of becoming emotionally healthy. For some, emotions become too much to bear and intervention is needed, such as counselling.

Childline offers adolescents support in several ways – including one-to-one online counselling chats. The Childline website (www.childline. org.uk) also offers many other youth-friendly services and information.

The NSPCC have a section of their website (www.nspcc.org. uk) dedicated to helping professionals protect children. It includes research, training and advice on how to support the younger generation's wellbeing.

Pause for thought

Take a moment to ponder the following questions.

- How do you cope with your emotions? Are you aware of different skills you use to cope with different feelings?

– Do your relationships with other Christians include exploring your emotions? Do you discuss how Jesus coped with his emotions during difficult life experiences?

– In day-to-day life, do you manage your emotions or do you let them build up until you explode?

– How could your spiritual life be enhanced by managing your feelings in a healthier way?

Workshop

This workshop is all about exploring different techniques for coping with emotions. There is no final list and everyone will find some skills more helpful than others. The important part is to encourage young people to try new techniques, especially if they are not used to discussing emotions. Inspiring and supporting young people to explore trickier aspects of life will lay a lasting foundation for their futures.

Moving forward

A great way to continue exploring emotions is by using the Talking About Emotions playing cards mentioned in the workshop. They can be a useful tool as an icebreaker or a more focused activity in small groups. Encourage the young people to use their emotional vocabulary in future and discover other techniques for managing their emotions.

Coping with emotions

(Annotated Workshop Outline)

Resources Needed

- Talking About Emotions playing cards (These can be purchased from youthscape.co.uk/store or you could create your own.)
- Score board
- Pens
- Post-it notes
- Coloured paper
- Print-outs of the Positive Action list
- Writing paper

Aim:

To explore how we cope with our emotions.

Leader's Notes:

It's helpful to use this as a follow-on from the 'Identifying Emotions' workshop but it can work as a standalone session too. Even though the primary aim of the workshop is to explore coping with emotions, it can also be a helpful time to learn more about one another and help unite the youth group. It is designed to be run as different stations that the young people walk around. Each activity has an explanation that can be printed and displayed next to the station.

Introduction

Begin the workshop by gathering the whole group together. Explain that today is all about exploring how we cope with our emotions. It's a chance to learn from others, learn more about ourselves and connect with God. Explain the different stations and you're all set to go!

It's helpful to have a few examples already written at the different stations. This could help the young people dive into the activities. Walk around the stations throughout the workshop yourself and engage in conversations with the young people.

Station 1: Snap with a twist

This station explores our emotions from different angles – including understanding emotions, coping with emotions, expressing emotions and emotional perspective. Create a score board and offer a prize for the winner! If purchasing the playing cards isn't an option for you, then you can make your own. An alternative could be using a normal pack of playing cards and writing a list of questions/statements that explore emotions. Match the suit, number or colour to the questions, and each time there is a snap read out the related question.

Explanation: Here's a pack of special cards. Your task is to play snap and become the ultimate winner! The twist is, each time you snap, you have to answer the question or statement that is on the card. Whoever wins by having all the cards at the end gets their name written on the score board. There will be a prize for the person who scores the highest! Remember – it is not a race. You must answer the question properly or you could be stripped of your winning title!

Before you run the session, take a moment to explore the playing cards yourself. This way, you'll be prepared to answer any of the questions yourself or help others answer them. Instead of playing snap, you can always play it so everyone takes a card and the person who has the highest card answers their question/statement. Don't be afraid of being strict – use the scoring as a way to encourage the group to engage with the cards.

Station 2: Healthy vs unhealthy

This station explores how we cope with emotions and whether we think that is a healthy or unhealthy way of managing our feelings. At the end, you should have a selection of suggested healthy and unhealthy post-it notes on each example.

Create two images of people out of coloured paper and write 'sad' and 'angry' above each. Make sure you don't place them too close together and identify one side of each as healthy and one as unhealthy. Have a pile of post-it notes and pens ready for the group to use.

Explanation: Here are two people. One represents us when we are sad and the other when we are angry. Use the post-it notes provided to write down what you do to cope when you feel those emotions. Think of as many ways as possible and write each one down on separate post-it notes. Then, decide if they are healthy or unhealthy ways of coping and stick them on the right side of the person.

For example, when you are angry you could punch a wall. Decide if that is a healthy or unhealthy way to manage your feelings of anger, then stick the post-it note under the correct heading.

This is an opportunity to learn more about how individuals in your group understand what healthy and unhealthy coping strategies look like – particularly for those most vulnerable. Challenge the young people's comments and engage in debate over whether something is healthy or unhealthy. Ask them to explain why they have written it down or think it's healthy/unhealthy. Use other people's post-it note answers as a way to help more timid members of the group participate in the activity.

Station 3: Take-away techniques

This station offers positive actions that can help us manage different emotions. Create a poster with the following actions and ask the young people to write down three (or more!) actions they could do to help their emotional health. You could even create an a6 card for them to write down the actions and keep in their wallet or pocket.

Explanation: Here's a whole bunch of different positive actions you can do to help manage your emotions. Pick a minimum of three actions and write them down. Keep that note on you to help you remember different actions you can take to develop your emotional health. Many of them are very general but try them, as they might just work for you!

Ask the young people whether they have engaged in any of these actions. Did it help? Why? Why not? What new action could they try? Is there a particular event coming up when they could put these actions into practice – such as exam stress, being alone during the school holidays, or doing a class presentation. This activity helps young people continue to learn and develop their emotional health after the workshop has finished. You could ask them about the actions they chose the next time you see them.

The Positive Actions List

Exercise – It's a great way to release feel-good chemicals in our brain, such as dopamine which helps us feel better. Plus, it's good for our physical health too!

Be kind to others – This can help take the focus off worrying about yourself but also brings joy to others.

Notice the good things in life – It's easier said than done, but sometimes just taking a moment to pause and think of three good things in your life can help lift your mood. Try it!

Talk it out – Sometimes it can be helpful to chat to a friend about what's on your mind and you can feel like the problem isn't as big any more.

Distract yourself – It's important to recognise how you're feeling and take note of that, but sometimes it can be helpful to distract yourself by watching a movie or heading out for a walk listening to music. It can elevate your mood and refresh your mind.

Don't give in to negative thoughts – We all have an internal monologue at times but if you find you're having negative thoughts, look for evidence against them. Are they really true? Or is it because you're having an 'off day' or you're under stressful circumstances that are out of your control? Don't let the negative thoughts win.

Get outside! – Instead of looking outside and seeing grey skies and rain, see it as an opportunity to jump in a puddle or skim stones on the water. Wrapping up and heading out for a walk on a cold day can get the blood circulating and boost your mood. Simply hang out with nature for a while. Fresh air is excellent medicine, plus it's free!

Be open and accept what is going on – It can be really hard to keep fighting life stressors and can leave you feeling exhausted. Sometimes it helps to pause, appreciate the positives in life and be aware of what is happening around you. Acknowledge your thoughts and feelings but don't overly engage with them for a moment, just 'be'.

Practise gratitude – Say thank you to others and show that you're grateful. Appreciate others and remember those positive moments.

Station 4: Prayer

This station is an opportunity to consciously connect with God in several different ways. It's all about helping the young people to recognise that God and emotions do mix – we are to partner with God. Prayer is a Christian practice that many undervalue, yet it can be so useful when it comes to managing our emotions – especially in the heat of the moment!

Explanation: Here's a chance to consciously connect with God. Spend some time thinking about how you cope with your emotions. Do you manage them in a healthy or unhealthy way? Is there a positive action you can do to help your emotions? Do you pray regularly or is it a one-off thing? Use this as a space to be still and reflect on all that you've learnt in this workshop. You could write a prayer letter to God, asking for help in how to handle a particular emotion or situation. It might be helpful to lie down and close your eyes, saying a silent prayer in your head. Perhaps you could gather together with a few friends to pray for one another.

If you have the resources, you could create a cosy corner with bean bags, reflective music, etc. for this station.

Begin to draw the session to a close by having an open discussion about how their spiritual lives could be affected by their emotional health. Can God help them to manage their emotions? Are there Christian practices such as praying that can help us?

Finish

There is no specific end to this workshop, which can last until everyone has had an opportunity to take part in all the stations. If time allows, you could gather the group together and ask if anyone found any stations particularly helpful and why. Let the young people know who to go to if they wish to discuss anything more and encourage them to use their positive actions in the coming weeks.

THREE

Self-esteem

Self-esteem is how a person feels about themselves and what they do. Someone with positive self-esteem will generally approach things thinking they are a good person who deserves love and support and can succeed in life. Someone with low or negative self-esteem will generally think they are not good at things, don't deserve love or support and that situations will work out badly for them.[6]

Having low self-esteem isn't a mental health problem in itself but, if it continues for a long period, then it can lead to illnesses such as anxiety or depression.

Everyone's self-esteem fluctuates throughout their lives and this is completely normal and healthy. Such fluctuation can be particularly apparent in adolescence, as this is a pivotal time for young people to form their identity within the wider world.

There is no set position as to where a person should or shouldn't be on their self-esteem scale, as it is different for everyone. Rather, the focus should be on maintaining a healthy medium between the two extremes.

High self-esteem

Characteristics of a person with high self-esteem may include:

- Confidence

- Ability to make friends easily

- Being prepared to try new things and adapt to change

---

6. Youngminds (2017), *About self-esteem* [online]. Available at: < http://www.youngminds.org. uk/for_parents/whats_worrying_you_about_your_child/self-esteem/about_self-esteem> [Accessed: 10 February 2017]

- Being proud of their achievements
- Trying to solve problems on their own, but being willing to ask for help if needed
- Admitting mistakes and learning from them
- Having a positive image of themselves.

Low self-esteem

Characteristics of a person with low self-esteem may include:

- Constantly comparing themselves to others in a negative way
- Inability to cope with failure
- Lack of confidence
- Regularly putting their self down
- Hesitant to try new things, if at all
- Finding change hard to handle
- Struggling to make and keep friends
- Feeling victimised by others.[7]

Life's circumstances

Everyone responds to life situations differently, with some coping better than others. The following are key events that could affect a person's self-esteem:

- Changing schools
- Moving house
- Starting a new job
- Changes in the family unit

---

7. Youngminds (2017), *About self-esteem* [online]. Available at: < http://www.youngminds.org. uk/for_parents/whats_worrying_you_about_your_child/self-esteem/about_self-esteem> [Accessed: 10 February 2017]

- Bereavement

- Long-term illnesses

- Bullying

- Struggling with school achievements

- Expectations of others (parents/carers, teachers, peers)

- Body image

- Abuse (physical, mental, emotional, verbal, spiritual).

Young people's self-esteem

Every young person is unique and experiences life differently, including their self-esteem levels. Stereotypically, girls are seen as having much lower self-esteem than boys. This is usually associated with physical appearance – weight, body shape, beauty, muscles, etc. Yet, with the rising increase in boys suffering from eating disorders, and the protein shake concoctions advertised by muscly men, surely self-esteem is an issue for both sexes?

- 69% of girls aged 7–21 feel like they are not good enough[8]

- 52% of girls aged 7–21 would not seek help because they feel uncomfortable talking about their feelings[9]

- 34% of adolescent boys have been on a diet to change their body shape or lose weight[10]

- 23% of boys thought they were 'too fat' when discussing their body image.[11]

8. Girlguiding (2016), *Girls Attitude Survey*. Available at: < https://www.girlguiding.org.uk/social-action-advocacy-and-campaigns/research/girls-attitudes-survey/> [Accessed: 10 February 2017]

9. Girlguiding (2016), *Girls Attitude Survey*. Available at: < https://www.girlguiding.org.uk/social-action-advocacy-and-campaigns/research/girls-attitudes-survey/> [Accessed: 10 February 2017]

10. Central YMCA (2016), *The Challenge of Being Young in Modern Britain*. Available at: < www.ymca.co.uk/content/pdf/World-of-Good-report-Central-YMCA.pdf> [Accessed: 10 February 2017]

11. HSCIC (2015), *Health and Wellbeing of 15 year olds in England: Findings from the What About YOUth Survey 2014*. Available at: < http://content.digital.nhs.uk/catalogue/PUB19244/what-about-youth-eng-2014-rep.pdf> [Accessed: 28 April 2017]

Self-esteem in Christ

Self-esteem can be like a roller-coaster for some people. If a person has high self-esteem, sometimes our British culture suggests they're being arrogant or smug. In the Church, we could be viewed as not being Christ-like, projecting self-importance above the image of Christ's. Low self-esteem, on the other hand, can be seen as dismissive of ourselves in society, or can give rise to guilt for not loving ourselves as God sees us.

The problem comes when our self-esteem hinders our ability to live up to the commandment to love God fully and our neighbour as ourselves. Christians do not need to have over-inflated views of themselves to be acceptable. God makes everyone worthy of his love and saves all through Christ Jesus. As a result, a person's real self-esteem is found in their relationship with Christ – not in self-criticism or human criticism.

Pause for thought

Spend some time exploring Matthew 22:36-40. How do you love your neighbour as yourself? Is this something you could develop on? How does your self-esteem fluctuate? Do you love yourself as God loves you? How does the knowledge of God's love for you affect your own self-esteem? It may be helpful to discuss this with a friend.

Further information

Here are a few suggestions of where to go next:

- The charity Mind offers up-to-date information on mental health and emotional wellbeing – www.mind.org.uk

- Family Lives offers support for parents/carers – www.familylives.org.uk

- The charity Esteem focuses on supporting adolescents who have either been through the Statutory Care system or are classified as 'NEET' (not in employment, education or training) – www. esteem.org.uk

- ADHD and You offers support for those with ADHD (attention deficit hyperactivity disorder) who suffer from low self-esteem – www.adhdandyou.co.uk

Workshop

It is important for young people to understand self-esteem and what can affect it. This workshop focuses on ourselves and explores what brings our self-esteem up and what brings it down. It highlights how different every person is and provides an opportunity to be vulnerable with one another by sharing our own self-esteem highs and lows.

Moving forward

Self-esteem is a topic that can be discussed in all sorts of ways. Try to de-bunk the myth that it is only girls who experience low self-esteem, since boys do as well. Use opportunities in day-to-day discussion with the group to lift their self-esteem and challenge unhelpful comments. As with all of the workshops, this is designed to be the beginning of a discussion rather than definitive.

Self-esteem

(Annotated Workshop Outline)

Resources Needed
- Bowl
- Paper cup
- Jug/bottle of water
- Pin

Aim:
To explore the highs and lows of our own self-esteem

Leader's Notes:
The cup and water activity can be a particularly sensitive activity. Be aware of your group and provide a space for them to chat more if they need to.

Don't forget to look after yourself, too. Hearing the challenges young people face and their vulnerabilities being on show can be emotionally draining. Schedule some time afterwards to chat with your supervisor or a trusted friend to process the workshop.

What is self-esteem?
Begin the workshop by having an informal conversation with the group about the topic of self-esteem.
What does the word 'self-esteem' mean?
What does it look like?
If someone asked you to explain it, what would you say?

This short task is a simple way to introduce the topic and focus the group. The young people will most likely be able to define this topic quite quickly, so don't feel pressured to drag out a conversation unnecessarily. The primary focus of the workshop is the cup and water activity, so if you're on a tight schedule, then keep this task short and sweet!

Highs and lows

After defining self-esteem, now is the time to identify the highs and lows of self-esteem. Using a whiteboard or wall space, write two headings – 'Highs' and 'Lows'. Give everyone in the group two post-it notes, and ask them to write down one thing that could bring up a person's self-esteem on the first post-it note. Then ask them to write one thing that could bring it down on another post-it note. Stick the post-it notes under the correct heading so everyone can see them. Take a moment to run through the different examples that are on the wall, explaining that they will be useful for the next activity.

It might be helpful to have two different-coloured post-it notes to distinguish the difference even more, or to put them on opposite sides of the room. Encourage the young people to chat to one another and help each other with examples. Use this as a time to prepare the group for the next activity by walking around and engaging them in conversation about the examples they have written.

Cup and water activity

This is an opportunity to be open and honest as a youth group. It's a chance to find common ground between one another, realising that no one's self-esteem is perfect. This activity can empower everyone in the group to know they can lift their own self-esteem.

This is the time to bring the group into a safe atmosphere, getting rid of any nervous laughter and recognising that this doesn't have to be a boring serious experience but a chance to become closer as a group. It may be helpful to do a couple of breathing exercises to help calm the mood.

1. Ask the group to stand in a circle and explain that the cup represents us (you could draw a face on it if you want!) and the water represents our self-esteem. Fill the cup half way with water, putting it in the bowl in the centre of the circle.

2. Explain that one by one you're going to go into the centre of the circle, saying one thing that brings your self-esteem down. As you say it, use the pin to pierce the cup. As each person pierces the cup, water will begin to slowly drip out (this is why the bowl is useful!). Go round multiple times, encouraging everyone to be honest in their answers.

   If you think your group needs an incentive, you could always put a selection of sweets next to the bowl. Each person can then take a sweet once they've shared a comment. The twist is, if they don't give an answer then they can't take a sweet.

3. Pause the group when it feels right and explain that each time you pierce a hole in the cup, it's like a bad experience or a negative comment that lowers our self-esteem. This can be seen by the water slowly dripping out. Explain that sometimes we can shrug off that rude comment or that low grade but, over time, it can substantially lower our self-esteem. We can see that as our self-esteem level – or the water level in the cup – goes down, eventually we could end up with no self-esteem.

   If time allows, now could be a good time to discuss what someone with no or very low self-esteem looks like.

4. Share with the group that everyone's self-esteem gets lowered at times and this may not be our fault, but we do have the power to 'top up' our self-esteem level. Pick up the jug of water and explain that this time you're going to share one thing that brings your self-esteem up, pouring a little of the 'self-esteem water' into the cup.

5. Close the activity by explaining that everyone's self-esteem levels are different. What brings one person's self-esteem up, may bring

another's down. This shows how different everyone is. Perhaps as a result of hearing what brings other people's self-esteem up, you could try their ideas when you're having a rough day. Encourage the group to remember they have the power to lift their self-esteem, and no one can take that away from them.

Don't forget to use the ideas that were written on the post-it notes to help the group. It's fine for someone to repeat what another group member has said but encourage them to think for themselves.

If your youth group is particularly close and meets regularly, it may be helpful to take this activity a step further by helping the members be accountable for lifting one another's self-esteem.

End on a high

It's important to lift the mood of the group as the atmosphere can become fragile during the activity. It might be helpful to play a quick game to help everyone leave on a positive note. Remind the group of where to go for additional support if they felt that was needed. Challenge everyone to do one thing that lifts their self-esteem this week – or even try something new! Close the session by praying for one another.

The next time you see the group it might be helpful to share something you have done to lift your own self-esteem. Ask around and see if anyone tried anything new, or if the activity helped them recognise when their self-esteem was lowered.

FOUR

Anxiety

Anxiety is a word we use to describe feelings of unease, worry and fear. It incorporates both the emotions and the physical sensations we might experience when we are worried or nervous about something. Although we usually find it unpleasant, anxiety is related to the 'fight or flight' response – our normal biological reaction to feeling threatened.[12]

Understanding anxiety

Everyone experiences anxiety from time to time in their lives and, even though unpleasant, it is completely normal. For example, sitting an exam or starting a new job are both scenarios where a person may feel particularly tense and/or nervous. They may suffer from poor sleep or struggle to eat, due to feelings of sickness. Once the exam has been sat or the first period of a new job is over, anxiety passes and you can continue with life as normal.

Anxiety can become a cause for concern when it affects a person's day-to-day life for a prolonged period. This could mean consistently worrying about normal daily activities or even worrying about worrying. Experiencing symptoms of anxiety, even after a particular situation has passed, can be a sign that support is needed. Such extensive anxiety is a serious mental health illness and the long-term effects can include a lowered immune system, insomnia, depression and more.

Signs and symptoms

The following is a list of physical and psychological indicators of anxiety:

- Muscle tension

- Nausea

---

12. Mind (2015), *Anxiety and panic attacks* [online]. Available at <http://www.mind.org.uk/information-support/types-of-mental-health-problems/anxiety-and-panic-attacks/about-anxiety/#.WKbhABh0fVo> [Accessed: 17 February 2017]

- Difficulty sleeping

- Feeling 'on edge'

- Restlessness

- Sweating

- Hot flushes

- Feeling a sense of numbness

- Pins and needles

- Fearing the worst/sense of dread

Anxiety disorders

It is important to remember that 'anxiety' is an umbrella word – it has other anxiety-related disorders underneath it. Usually, when we use the term 'anxiety', we are referring more specifically to 'generalised anxiety disorder', also known as GAD. Other anxiety disorders are:

- Panic disorder

- Obsessive-compulsive disorder (OCD)

- Phobias

- Post-traumatic stress disorder (PTSD).

Anxiety and adolescents

Young people are experiencing anxiety more commonly than ever before. It is becoming a lifestyle that adolescents experience and are having to acclimatise to. Worries and concerns about themselves, their families and friends, along with the wider world, are filling the younger generation's minds daily.

Young people are trying to navigate many tensions – from seeing the response to global terrorist attacks trending on Twitter, to sitting in a classroom while teachers pile on the pressures of exams. But where is God in all of this? Where are his people showing the way like Christ did, facing adversity with a growing faith?

Letting God into the picture

Imagine if the church became a place where our fears, worries and concerns were welcomed and our vulnerabilities were embraced. Imagine young people walking into the youth club knowing they could safely share their anxieties and be equipped with Christ-like skills to face life's stressors. This is the direction our youth work needs to go if we are truly combining spiritual development with exploring our psychological health.

Resilience

Anxiety is often seen through the lens of negativity. It can be seen as a weakness of not being able to cope with life or as an accepted flaw in the human make-up – a 'worry wart', as many proclaim. It's important to seek support when it has a negative effect on a person's quality of life. It's also important to recognise when we are experiencing anxiety over normal life and to use it as a tool to build resilience – rather than completely break.

Youth leaders are in the privileged position of being able to support adolescents in facing life's stressors in a positive way. By teaching young people the signs and symptoms, along with coping mechanisms on how to face an exam or start their first weekend job, we can help build a resilient person. Subsequently, this can help them in all areas of their life – including their faith.

We can help a young person see that, just because God didn't respond to their prayer request the first time – or perhaps didn't respond in the way they wanted him to – doesn't mean they should get stressed out and give up. Instead, this is perhaps an opportunity to embrace the unknown rather than becoming overwhelmed by it.

Looking ahead

Anxiety doesn't have to become debilitating. There is treatment out there which looks different for everyone. Most commonly, reviewing a person's daily lifestyle is a helpful place to start. How is their diet?

Are they being fuelled by caffeine and sugar? Or are they shattered because they aren't eating anything? How is the person's sleep? Are they exhausted because they can't rest properly? Is exercise a part of their daily routine?

Having a safe space in which to share thoughts and feelings can be extremely helpful and a great tool to teach adolescents as they mature into adulthood. This could be in the form of mentoring or more formally through Cognitive Behavioural Therapy (CBT) or counselling that a GP can refer a person to.

In some cases, medication may be used to help manage the physical and psychological symptoms so the person can focus on learning strategies and tools of how to cope in life.

Further information

There are many places to search for more information on anxiety and anxiety disorders. Here are a few:

- Anxiety UK – www.anxietyuk.org.uk/

- NHS website – www.nhs.uk/pages/home.aspx

- The Mental Health Foundation – www.mentalhealth.org.uk/

- Mind, the mental health charity – www.mind.org.uk/

Moodjuice (www.moodjuice.scot.nhs.uk/) is a website created by the NHS which helps people of all ages think about their emotional health. It provides several resources that can be used to help understand a specific illness and ways to manage it.

Along with exploring anxiety through Bible studies and prayer, many Christians have found *The Worry Book* by Will van der Hart and Rob Waller a useful resource.[13] It combines theology and psychology to offer different perspectives and opportunities for reflection.

---

13. W. Hart and R. Waller (2011), *The Worry Book,* InterVarsity Press.

Pause for thought

Anxiety can affect anyone – including you. Take a moment to think about your work with young people. Are there any areas that cause you anxiety? Is that OK because it is new and exciting, or does it cause sleepless nights and nausea? Is there a young person you are particularly anxious about? Why? Is there something you can do to support them or someone else who could offer support? How do you manage anxiety when it appears from common life stressors? Pause and contemplate these questions for a moment before heading into the workshop section.

Workshop

The following workshop offers a basic understanding of anxiety. This is explored through statistical facts, life experiences and the biblical exploration of 'casting your cares' found in 1 Peter 5:7.

To run an effective workshop on anxiety, or any emotional health topic, it's important you know what you're talking about. Read this chapter again and research any areas you may not understand. Be as informed as possible so you can offer your young people correct information and a useful reflection time.

Moving forward

Take a moment to reflect on how the previous workshop went. Are there future workshops you could run around anxiety, based on discussions today? How could the wider church support the youth group in their anxieties? Would it be helpful to hear a testimony from an older church member about how anxiety and faith mix for them? Did any young people stand out to you who might benefit from a one-to-one conversation? It may be helpful to sit and reflect on these questions with a volunteer or your supervisor.

Anxiety

(Annotated Workshop Outline)

Resources Needed
- Large paper and pens
- Large vase of water
- Dissolvable vitamins
- 1 Peter 5:7

Aim:

To learn more about anxiety and take part in a practical response to 'casting our cares'.

Leader's Notes:

We know how real anxiety can be and how much it can affect our lives. We want to support our young people as much as possible, so don't forget to remind them that there is hope and advise them on where to go for additional support.

The topic of anxiety isn't as much of a taboo subject as other mental illnesses. This could mean that your group already has a basic understanding of the topic. Be aware of this and use it as an opportunity to hear from the young people.

Human knot!

DO: Have the group stand in a circle facing the middle. Ask them to reach their right arm towards the centre and grab someone else's hand. Make sure no one holds the hand of the person right next to them. Then do the same with the left arm. The group then work together to untangle the human knot they have created. They can go over and under each other's arms and legs but they must NOT break the chain of connected hands in the process. You could even have a few groups race each other!

This is a simple physical activity to get the session started and introduce the topic. Here is a great place to briefly ask what the group knows about anxiety. Then you'll be able to gauge a basic understanding of where their knowledge is at. This can then inform you how long or short the following activities need to be, for them to be most useful to your specific group.

At the end, explain that sometimes anxiety can be like a knot in our stomach. Sometimes it can untangle quickly and our anxiety is reduced. Other times it feels like more and more knots are evolving in our stomach, like a bunch of Russian dolls, and anxiety takes over our mind and body. This week we're going to explore this topic and what the Bible says about it.

Umbrella of anxiety

SAY: Anxiety is like an umbrella with lots of different conditions underneath. This could be OCD, social anxiety, panic attacks, and more. Did you know that one in six young people will experience an anxiety condition at some point in their lives? That means that up to five people in your class at school may be living with anxiety! Anxiety is something we ALL face at different points in our lives but when it begins to negatively affect our daily lives – we need to seek help. But first, let's think about what situations could result in us experiencing anxiety.

You could ask a volunteer to draw an umbrella on a white board and write the different conditions underneath to help the visual learners in the group. Later, you could refer back to the illustration as a tool for further discussion. This is one way of maximising the resource given to you through this workshop.

Real-life experiences

DO: Split the group into pairs and ask them to think of one real-life situation where someone could experience anxiety. This could be right before they take a music exam or when they walk into a room that is already full of people; from being introduced to a step-parent, to handing in a school project you've been working on day and night.

After giving them time to think, go around and share the different situations. Are any of them the same? Does everyone agree or do some get anxious about something that others aren't bothered about? Is there a theme that runs through this group's anxieties that you can pick up on?

Now's the time to de-bunk any myths or unhelpful comments around anxiety, reinforcing the fact that everyone experiences anxiety to some degree and, for some, it can become an illness which requires additional support. This is an opportunity to see where your group associate anxiety with their lives and even learn more about them. Ask yourself – in future sessions, is there anything I can cover which will help the group deal with their anxieties?

Mind, body and soul

DO: Ask for a volunteer and draw around them on a large piece of paper so you have an outline of a human. Ask the group to write on the paper what they think anxiety is like. For example, in the brain you could draw a thought bubble with anxious thoughts like 'I'm nervous about the school play' or 'I'm worried they don't like me.' Where the heart is meant to be, you could draw a heart that is racing away to show an elevated heart rate. Provoke a discussion around their spiritual lives – how does anxiety affect their relationship with God? Encourage the group to get creative!

SAY: Looking at the human we have created, we can see how much anxiety can affect different areas of our lives – from our minds to our bodies to our souls. We can see how different it is for everyone and recognise that it's OK to experience it differently.

For some young people in your group, they may feel a strong sense of relief at hearing you say that it's OK to experience anxiety – especially as a Christian – in different ways. Others may never have associated their faith and the physiological effects anxiety can have together. This is a helpful time to share some of your own anxious thoughts and feelings. Take time over this exercise and split them up into smaller groups if that works better for your group.

Good news!

SAY: The good news is that we can learn to control our anxieties and we don't have to face them alone – hooray! In 1 Peter chapter 5 verse 7, we are reminded to cast our cares on God because God cares for us. These powerful words are so helpful to remember if we are suffering from anxiety.

ASK: Does anyone know what the words 'cast your cares' means?

SAY: Casting our cares is offering our anxieties to God. Its action is us praying to God and giving our anxieties to him, trusting that he will take care of the situation. We can cast our cares on God because he cares for us – it's an amazing feeling to know that our loving Father cares for us. He loves us so much that he wants our anxieties to become more manageable. He cares for each and every one of us – no matter how anxious we get!

ASK: Is it easy to cast our cares on God? Does it come naturally to you? Do you believe God cares for us?

Try and go deeper than typical surface conversation answers. Push your group to think deeper and be honest about their answers. If they are particularly quiet, ask them to speak to the person next to them and be ready to feedback one answer to the rest of the group. Are any of the answers the same? Is there a resounding 'no' or 'yes' to believing God cares for them? Is this something you could explore in future sessions? Use your intuitive skills to know how far to push the conversation.

Vitamins and water

SAY: Imagine these tablets are like our anxieties (give examples of ones that have been discussed through the session). Each time you offer your anxieties to God, it's like dropping a tablet in the water – the anxiety is diluted in God's hand. The cause of the anxiety may not disappear, but the effect on us is less concentrated.

DO: Standing in a circle, ask the group to take a tablet in their hand and silently think of an anxiety they are experiencing. Ask them to take turns to put the tablet in the water as a symbol of casting that anxiety on God, remembering he cares for us. Repeat this as necessary.

Silence can be particularly challenging for some youth groups. If that is the case, it may be helpful to set a time limit of silence or ask two people to go up at once to help speed up the time that is needed for silence. Be encouraged not to shy away from this activity just because it needs a little preparation and/ or because it's different from your usual youth work. Embrace it as a time to be vulnerable and experience a reflective time together as a group. You may even want to repeat this activity! Warning: the tablets may fizz more than you realise, so make sure you don't overload the vase with them all at once!

Pray

Ask the group to put their right hand on the right shoulder of the person standing on their right-hand side. Then, encourage the young people to pray for the person their hand is touching to know that they can cast their cares on God because he cares for them.

Challenge

As a way of moving forward, challenge the group to think – what one anxiety do you have that you could begin to face this week knowing that God cares for you? Report back to us next session.

It's really important that the conversation doesn't end here. Encourage them to take part in the challenge and set a reminder for yourself to ask them how it went the next time you're together.

FIVE

Depression

Depression is a common mental disorder, characterised by sadness, loss of interest or pleasure, feelings of guilt or low self-worth, disturbed sleep or appetite, feelings of tiredness, and poor concentration.[14]

In its mildest form, depression is a persistent low mood. You are able to continue with your daily activities, like taking a shower or brushing your teeth, but they can feel much harder to complete and not worthwhile doing. In its most severe form, depression can be a life-threatening illness, leading to suicidal thoughts and acts.

Did you know . . . ?

- Globally, an estimated 350 million people of all ages suffer from depression.

- In the UK, the proportion of young people who reported that they frequently had feelings of depression or anxiety doubled between the mid-1980s and 2000s.

- More women are affected by depression than men.

- It is the leading cause of disability worldwide.[15]

What symptoms should I look out for?

It is normal for children, young people and adults to feel low or 'blue' at times in their lives. However, when the signs of depression continue for a couple of weeks and start to interfere with day-to-day life, it could become an illness.

---

14. World Health Organisation (2015), *Depression* [online]. Available at: <http://www.who.int/topics/depression/en/> [Accessed: 30th October 2016]
15. Ibid.

Symptoms of depression include, but are not limited to, the following:

- Feelings of hopelessness

- Becoming self-critical

- Low or no energy

- Loss of interest in hobbies you used to enjoy

- Excessive sleeping or not being able to sleep

- Avoiding normal social situations or commitments

- A desire to self-harm.

Depression has no preferences for whom it attacks – children, young people or adults – everyone is susceptible to this illness. Research does suggest, however, that some are more vulnerable to experiencing it than others. This could be from our genes, as indicated by other family members suffering from mental illness. It could also be a reaction to life stressors, such as family breakdown, abuse or bullying. There is no single cause.

A big question in our society today – is depression caused by a chemical imbalance?

This is a hard question to answer as there are many layers to it but, according to Mind, the simple answer is no.[16] Quite often this question is born out of the idea that taking anti-depressants changes the brain's chemistry and somehow 'corrects' it. Currently, the evidence for this is very weak and we simply don't know if this 'correction' of brain chemistry is the result of depression or its cause. But what we do know is that some who take anti-depressants find it brings them into a better mental state to then continue to experience life more fully and tackle any underlying issues. There is no shame in taking anti-depressants and this shaming

---

16. Mind (2016), *What causes depression* [online]. Available at: <http://www.mind.org.uk/information-support/types-of-mental-health-problems/depression/causes/#.WKq0Zxh0fVo> [Accessed: 17 February 2017]

must be banished from our society. The brain is incredibly complex and there is much more research that needs to be done to understand how depression and the brain mix.

The Church

Within our Christian society there are various misconceptions that we can fall into believing – such as 'Christians are meant to be joyful, therefore we can't get depressed' or 'You're not believing enough that God can heal, so you're not being healed.' These untruths have spread like wild fire and it's time we politely corrected those who repeat them.

When you're a young person in church suffering from depression, it can be an extremely isolating experience. It can feel as though no one believes you've actually got an illness because you aren't physically on crutches. Others may just think they're being a normal 'moody teenager' who's experiencing a burst of hormones. Put yourself in their shoes for a moment and think what it would be like to walk into your church while suffering from depression.

Hope versus hopelessness

Depression can lead to a sense of hopelessness. However, what is so wonderful about the gospel is that it is full of hope and this should be reflected in our churches. From the dodgy tax collectors to the Psalm writers who pour their hearts out – there is hope for all.

The good news is there is hope for healing in multiple ways. This can be down the western medicine route of therapy such as CBT, counselling and/or anti-depressants. As Christians, we can pray for one another, asking the Father with grateful hearts to heal us. As the Church, we can educate ourselves more on the topic of depression and guide others to suitable support networks.

Further information

There are a lot of excellent – and not so excellent – places to look. Be smart when looking up information on the internet – remember, anyone can publish something online. Some of the most useful charitable sources are:

- Time to Change – www.time-to-change.org.uk/

- Mind – www.mind.org.uk/

- Heads Together – www.headstogether.org.uk/

- ThinkTwice – www.thinktwiceinfo.org/

You might find it helpful to pop into your local GP surgery. Often they have leaflets of local support groups, private counselling services and general information pamphlets.

One way of gaining a deeper biblical understanding around depression is to study the Book of Job. It is a complex book with many layers, yet Job suffered severe depression and expresses himself throughout the book. To delve into it effectively, it might be helpful to use a Bible commentary to help unpack Job's experiences and God's work.

Pause for thought

Take a moment to think of the young people in your church – do you know if any of them suffer from depression? Have you noticed symptoms of depression in a young person? Are they experiencing depression to the point where they need professional help or is it a persistent low mood that needs to be kept an eye on?

Workshop

Many adolescents suffer from depression and Christians are not exempt. This session equips young people with key facts about this illness and a strategy that Jesus used in Matthew to face it with. It explores what depression is like from a biblical perspective and ends with a simple reflective activity.

Before running the session take a moment to get clued up on the topic. Use the information provided in this booklet as a start and the suggested reading for more information. You want to be able to have a basic understanding so you can correctly and informatively educate your youth group.

Moving forward

It's really important not to end the discussion on depression here, but rather use this workshop as a baseline for future conversations. It may be that you offer an informal conversation around this topic in the weeks that follow or you use social media to promote advice. You could even create your own workshops on 'How to support a friend with depression' or a Bible study evening dedicated to Job. The possibilities really are endless, so get thinking!

Depression

(Annotated Workshop Outline)

Resources Needed
- Bibles/print-outs of Matthew 26:37-39
- Print-outs of 'Depression is like . . .'

Aim:

To be a starting point for gaining a basic understanding of depression, and how Jesus brings us all hope.

Keep your aim in mind throughout the session – it'll help keep you focused and bring back any conversation that goes wandering onto different topics.

Leader's Notes:

It's important that you offer support for those who may need it after the session has ended. Everyone is susceptible to experiencing bouts of depression, but for some it is an illness that requires further intervention. Be sure to know your safeguarding policy in case you need to take action. Remember, talking about depression doesn't have to be a solemn experience – embrace the laughter of games and the joy Jesus brings!

Your safeguarding policy should be a live document, ever changing to support your young people to the best of your knowledge. Keep an eye on it and make sure others, such as volunteers, are familiar with it too. It may be helpful to brief any volunteer you have on this before the session starts. Talking about depression can be daunting – so address anxieties volunteers have beforehand, so you can run the session to the best of your ability.

Introduction

SAY: Depression is a huge topic! It's one word that has so much linked to it and we're going to start discovering that today. A helpful definition of depression is from the World Health Organisation which says, *'Depression is a common mental disorder, characterised by sadness, loss of interest or pleasure, feelings of guilt or low self-worth, disturbed sleep or appetite, feelings of tiredness, and poor concentration.'*

You can begin to unpack the definition further in the true and false activity with the group. It is important young people understand that depression isn't always extreme to the point of suicide but rather an illness that many face and can live with when they receive support.

You could use this as a chance to ask a volunteer to read out the definition so there is a mixture of voices. You may wish to include symptoms or other aspects that are written in the chapter.

Continue to explain to the group that depression appears in both the Old and New Testaments and people are experiencing it this very day. It's real and it's time to start getting clued up about it.

True or false?

This activity is really about getting rid of any inhibitions or anxieties young people have around talking about depression whilst at the same time debunking myths! It's about letting your youth group know that you're willing to openly discuss this tough topic and that you can do it whilst having fun. It's a chance to get the group physically moving around and even get the competitive side out of them! Asking someone to be a 'quiz master' is an opportunity to empower a particular individual, so have a think about who this person could be beforehand. If it is a particularly reserved or new member of the group, then perhaps take them on one side and ask them privately beforehand, so as not to embarrass them if they say no or feel like they have to say yes.

DO: Identify one end of the room as true and the other end as false. Read out the following statements – or create more of your own – and ask the group to run to the side they think is correct, and then re-centre the group after each statement is read. You could even ask one of the group members to be the 'quiz master'!

1. You can snap out of depression just by thinking positively.
   FALSE: Depression is a serious illness. Many never seek treatment but people can get better with the right support.

2. The best way to help someone who is depressed is to try and cheer them up.
   FALSE: The best way to help someone is to encourage them to seek out help by speaking to a person they trust and heading to their GP.

3. Christians can't suffer from depression.
   FALSE: Christians can suffer from depression, just as they can suffer from the flu or any other illness.

4. One in ten children and young people are affected by a mental health problem.
   TRUE: That's around three students in every class!

5. No one in the Bible suffered from depression or depressive symptoms.
   FALSE: A whole heap of people did – Elijah, Job, Moses, Jonah, Jeremiah and even Jesus!

Gather the group together at the end and ask if anyone knew the answers already. Have a mini-discussion at this point about what they do and don't already know about depression.

This is a time to briefly determine how much knowledge the group have on depression. For example, did any of the young people disagree with the answers? If so, why? Use that as an opportunity to challenge their thoughts

— why do they think that? Who did they learn that from? How do they feel about three students in every class being affected by a mental health problem? If you didn't know some of these points, then you can even share that you learnt something too when planning the workshop – providing an example that it is OK not to know everything and we are all here to learn.

Depression is like . . .

SAY: Talking about our emotional health can be difficult at times, especially when it comes to explaining what it feels like.

DO: Lay out the following verses face-down and ask each person to pick one up and read it out in turn. Use this time to discuss any reflections the group has on these descriptions of what depression is like.

This is a chance to bring the Bible alive to your young people. This could even be the first time that the Lord's words have truly connected with them. The deep pain that is coming from these words shouldn't be taken lightly. Additionally, some of your youth group may even resonate with some of these passages – don't shy away from that but, if it's more appropriate for a one-to-one conversation, then explain that and crack on with the rest of the workshop. Remember that these are verses with context, so read around them so you know the wider background.

1. My guilt has overwhelmed me like a burden too heavy to bear. *Psalm 38:4*

2. Why, my soul, are you downcast? Why so disturbed within me? *Psalm 42:11*

3. [Elijah] came to a broom bush, sat down under it and prayed that he might die. 'I have had enough, Lord,' he said. 'Take my life; I am no better than my ancestors.' *1 Kings 19:4*

4. 'Now, Lord, take away my life, for it is better for me to die than to live.' *Jonah 4:3*

5. 'My soul is overwhelmed with sorrow to the point of death.'
Matthew 26:38

Jesus' strategy

This is about delving into the life of Jesus and giving young people a practical way to begin to learn how to manage their emotional health. It's an opportunity to relate, in some way, to Jesus and continue to learn that the Bible is just as relevant today as when it was written. Depending on where your group is at in terms of theological discussion, it might be helpful to use different versions of the Bible to explore this strategy.

SAY: As we look through the Bible at Jesus' life we can see that he also suffered from bouts of depression – just as you and I might do in our lives. We also know that Jesus brings us all hope! If we delve into Matthew's account in chapter 26, we can see how Jesus brings hope to depression. If we look closely, he demonstrates a strategy in Gethsemane of what to do when a bout of depression begins to take over, as a way of confronting and overcoming the overwhelming circumstances he faces.

DO: Ask a volunteer to read Matthew 26:37-39. You could even ask them to read it out like a monologue.

Again, another opportunity to empower an individual who perhaps doesn't normally get a chance to share. No matter our age or how long we've been in the church, we are all on a journey together to learn and become Christ-like beings; this is a chance to model this.

ASK: In pairs/small groups, ask them if they can identify the strategy Jesus uses.

Explain the strategy: There is no set way this needs to be done, so feel free to be as creative as you like, making sure it is clear. You could write each point down and make a flow chart out of them and ask the young people to annotate it – the possibilities are endless!

1. He chose close friends to be with at this difficult time (v.37)

2. He opened his soul to them, telling them how he felt (v.38)

3. He asked them to be with him (v.38)

4. He poured his heart out to the Father (v.39)

5. He rested his soul in God by trusting in his will (v.39)

Provoke a discussion around their thoughts and opinions of the strategy. Is it something they could do? How could the strategy look for them? Can they identify the close friends they could open their soul up to? What could it look like for them to rest their soul in God by trusting his will? Can they provide examples? The strategy can be used by anyone as a tool to help our emotional wellbeing.

Hope

Move your conversation on to focus on the hope we have as Christians. Explain that Jesus repeatedly prayed that God's will be done, *despite* how overwhelmed and hopeless he was feeling (v. 39, v. 42, v. 43). Take a moment to unpack this with the group. What do they think about this? Is this something they can relate to? Can they have hope in their own lives?

Prayers of hope

With some groups of young people it can be really easy to avoid having silent reflection time. This may be because they distract each other and can't sit still for very long. This is an opportunity to break that habit and realise how key it is to process all that you've just discussed.

It's important that everyone recognises that depression can seem like a bleak illness to discuss and/or experience; however, there IS hope and they can get better. Finding hope in depression goes beyond 'feeling hopeful' but believing it, even if you don't feel it.

Move your conversations on from inwardly thinking how Jesus brings hope to ourselves and think of the wider world. Explain that Jesus brings hope to our friends and family, to countries and nations – his hope is for everyone and that is glorious!

Ask everyone to find a space in the room to sit and pause, closing their eyes if that's helpful. Take a moment of silence to reflect on the busy session. Encourage them to pray for the wider world; for people persecuted for being Christians, for war-torn countries and the refugees fleeing their homes for safety; and for those feeling hopeless to become hopeful.

End note

Don't forget to remind young people of where they can go if they need extra support from this session.

SIX

Self-harm

Commonly, self-harm is understood as a physical response to an emotional pain. It can be a way of dealing with overwhelming feelings, painful memories or a sense of feeling out of control. When it becomes the default way to cope, a pattern of destructive behaviours soon develops, which can be both addictive and habitual.[17] [18] [19]

The term self-harm can be broken down into two sub-categories: harming behaviour and self-injury.

Harming behaviours are actions that have long-term health effects: smoking, drug misuse, risky sexual behaviour, under/over eating, to name a few. These are generally more socially acceptable behaviours which most people tend to engage in at some point in their lives.

Self-injury is to deliberately harm or injure oneself: cutting, burning, pinching, hair pulling, medication abuse, poisoning, and head banging all come under this category.[20]

How common is self-harm?

- About 25% of young people self-harm on one occasion, most commonly by cutting.[21]

    This doesn't mean that those 25% go on to continue self-harming. Adolescents are curious and, as with many other activities, they'll experiment with it once and then not do it again.

17. Selfharmuk (2017), *The facts: What is self-harm?* [online]. Available at: <https://www.selfharm. co.uk/get/facts/what_is_self-harm> [Accessed 7 February 2017]
18. Mind (2016), *Self-harm* [online]. Available at: <http://www.mind.org.uk/information-support/ types-of-mental-health-problems/self-harm/#.WJh53xh0fVo> [Accessed 7 February 2017]
19. Freedomfromharm, *Information Self-harm* [online]. Available at: <http://freedomfromharm. com/info/#selfharm> [Accessed 7 February 2017]
20. Selfharmuk (2016), SHUK Training Notes [word doc]. 7 February 2017: selfharmUK.
21. B. Wright, N. Hooke, S. Neupert et al (2013), 'Young people who cut themselves: can understanding the reasons guide the treatment?' *Advances in Psychiatric Treatment* 19: 446-456.

- The majority of people who are reported to self-harm are aged between 11 and 25.[22]

  Don't be blind. Self-harm can affect anyone; there is no 'typical' person who harms themselves.

- There has been a large increase in the number of adolescents admitted to hospital because of self-harm. Over the last ten years this figure has increased by 68%.[23]

  Hospital admissions can be very subjective, in that not all self-harm-related admissions are recorded accurately. Nevertheless, the drastic rise in patient numbers demonstrates the self-harm crisis we are facing.

Why self-harm?

Self-harming is not a mental illness but a behaviour that indicates a lack of coping skills. There are several illnesses that are associated with it, including depression, eating disorders and anxiety.

Many self-harm because of a difficult experience(s), such as bullying, abuse, the breakdown of a relationship, illness and/or stress. It can feel like a release from an overwhelming emotional state or an opportunity to feel something 'real' to replace emotional numbness. It is a coping mechanism that many find helps them manage life. It is not the same as attempting suicide, but must still be taken seriously.

Often, self-harm can be an indicator of a wider range of problems. These could include mental illness, dysfunctional family relationships, substance misuse, bullying, physical and sexual abuse.

How to respond

Youth leaders are in a privileged position to support adolescents who self-harm. It is usually in an informal setting where young people feel safe. Therefore, knowing how to respond is vital.

---

22. Mental Health Foundation (2017), *Self-harm* [online]. Available at: < https://www.mentalhealth.org.uk/a-to-z/s/self-harm> [Accessed 7 February 2017]
23. Youngminds (2011), '100,000 children and young people could be hospitalized due to self-harm by 2020 warns YoungMinds', London: YoungMinds.

If someone discloses that they self-harm, it is really important not to say: 'OMG! Why do you do that to yourself? Stop it immediately!'

Instead, share that you are grateful they have told you. Explain that you care and ask them how you can help. Remember to follow your safeguarding policy and to not promise that you will keep the disclosure a secret.

Self-harm is far more than someone cutting their arms. It can take many different forms and the reasons behind why a person chooses to self-harm are complex. Self-harm is a powerful communication of how intense emotional pain has become for someone, so your response is crucial.[24]

Attention Seeking

Calling someone an attention seeker because they self-harm is extremely dangerous and insensitive. It belittles both the person and the behaviour, and could prevent them from receiving support. Those who self-harm for attention are in distress and need support – not to be thoughtlessly labelled.

Self-harm and the Bible

There is no denying that there is a lack of credible theological insight into self-harm. It is a topic that hasn't generally been on the lips of biblical commentators. Yet it is a topic that affects many of God's people.

Further Information

There is a lot of support out there for those suffering from self-harm. One key place to begin would be researching the national organisation selfharmUK. Their website (www.selfharm.co.uk) is full of information for young people and professionals. Additionally, they offer training for anyone who works with young people.

www.freedomfromharm.com offers information and training around eating disorders and self-harm. It explores these topics as more than a

---

24. K. Middleton (2008), *Self Harm: The Path to Recovery*, Oxford, Lion Hudson.

teenage-only issue. It was established in response to the growing number of people in their 20s and 30s and beyond looking for support around self-harm and eating disorders, in a world that continues to see these struggles as teenage-only issues.

Pause for Thought

Take some time to reflect on the following points:

- Has self-harm affected your life – directly or indirectly?

- Imagine you encounter a young person who self-harms. How do you think God views them? Does he condemn them for actively harming their bodies, or does he hold them near, catching each tear they cry?

- Self-harm is not a sin, but a behaviour that shows emotional distress. How are you teaching your youth group to help others get the care they may need?

- Loving your neighbour includes promoting wellbeing. How do you promote wellbeing in your life?

Workshop

This workshop explores the topic of self-harm. It informs adolescents about self-harm by defining what self-harm is and isn't. Through de-bunking myths, young people learn the true facts about this topic. A reflection activity concludes the workshop, allowing participants time to pause and centre themselves before going back into their individual lives.

Moving forward

Self-harm is a topic that many feel ill-equipped to explore with young people, yet it is so needed. Find training in your area offered by charities or the local authority to help gain confidence and deliver effective education and support around this topic. Don't wait for someone else to explore this topic with your youth group or wait for young people themselves to bring it up. Be bold and begin this much needed conversation with adolescents.

Self-harm

(Annotated Workshop Outline)

Resources Needed
- Post-it notes
- Pens
- Print-out of fact and myth statements
- Pillar candle
- Tea lights
- Lighter
- Taboo cards

Aim:

To explore the topic of self-harm in a safe space and to support one another.

Leader's Notes:

Talking about self-harm can be challenging but please don't ignore this topic. Young people are smart and many of them are aware of self-harm to some degree. Use this as an opportunity to educate them, demonstrating that it's OK to talk about it. Please note that leading a session on self-harm can be emotionally exhausting, so remember to look after yourself. Self-harm doesn't have to be a taboo topic, but it does require self-awareness in order to support others effectively.

It might be helpful to check whether there is a fire alarm in the room and how sensitive it is. No one needs a fire alarm going off during a reflective moment!

If you have any other leaders or volunteers supporting your session, make sure you have a pre-workshop conversation with them. This is a great time to address any concerns they have before the workshop begins.

TABOO!

DO: This classic card game is all about guessing the word being described, without using any of the Taboo words listed on the card. One person selects a card to describe and the rest of the team have to guess. The more creative the clues, the better!

If you don't already have the card game, don't panic! There are many free printable copies which are easily found online; simply type 'taboo printable cards' in Google and there will be lots to choose from.

SAY: That game was all about taboo words and there are some words and topics we just don't talk about. Self-harm can be one of them, but today we're going to discuss it!

This is a good opportunity to ask them about what other topics are taboo, and whether they would like to discuss them in future workshops.

So, what is self-harm?

DO: Ask the young people to take a post-it note and answer the question: 'What is self-harm?' Take all the post-it notes in and give them a quick read so you can gauge how much the group knows.

SAY: The word 'self-harm' covers a few different areas.

- It can be physical, also known as 'self-injury', which is to deliberately harm/injure yourself (hair pulling, cutting, burning).

- It can be behavioural, also known as 'harming behaviours', that have a long-term health effect, like binge drinking or risky sexual behaviour.

- It's not always physical harm but can be emotionally harming ourselves, like judging ourselves really harshly or constantly putting ourselves down to a point where it affects our day-to-day lives.

Use the information at the start of the chapter to inform your explanation of what self-harm is and isn't. Don't overload your group with definitions but engage with them through the process, asking for examples or constructive comments.

Myth or fact?

SAY: There are a whole bunch of things being said about self-harm and the individuals who take part in it. It's all over the news and perhaps even in discussions in your schools. Now's the time to get our facts straight and bust myths around this topic!

DO: Split the group into teams, giving them a set of statements. Working together, ask the teams to make two piles of myths and facts, putting each statement in the pile they think is correct. When the teams have finished, go through the statements one at a time and ask them to explain why they've put it in the myths or facts pile. Afterwards, explain the correct answer. Use this as a time to openly discuss self-harm in a safe environment.

STATEMENT 1 – Only teenagers self-harm

MYTH: People of all ages can self-harm. It seems more common in teenagers as this is the age when people tend to begin self-harming and tell someone about it.

STATEMENT 2 – People self-harm because 'it feels nice'

MYTH: Self-harm is anything but nice. Often, people do it as a release of emotional pain they feel inside. Many people feel a rush of adrenalin before they harm, but then they feel the pain after that numbness has left.

STATEMENT 3 – You can get help if you self-harm

FACT: Everyone can get help. There are loads of people who can support you, including family, friends and health professionals. Self-harming is not an end point, but an opportunity to seek help and recover.

STATEMENT 4 – People self-harm just for attention

MYTH: It's really damaging to call someone an attention seeker. It's belittling their problem and saying they don't deserve help. We all need help and support at different times in our lives and sometimes this is a way of saying 'I need help'.

STATEMENT 5 – Self-harm is a suicide attempt

MYTH: Self-harm is very much a way of coping with life. By self-harming, people can feel they're being helped to get through day-to-day life.

SAY: There is so much information around self-harm and people have many assumptions about why a person is self-harming. We can use the information we've learnt from these myths and facts to help ourselves and others around this topic.

It may be that your group have other myths or facts they want to clear up. Now is a helpful opportunity to discuss them. If time doesn't allow this, then write them down and come back to them in the future.

What to do if you think someone is self-harming

DO: Ask the group to turn to the person next to them and think about what they would do if they thought someone they knew was self-harming. Ask volunteers to share their thoughts.

SAY: If you know someone is self-harming or has said to you that they are thinking of harming themselves, it's really important that you tell a trusted adult. They can then go on to help that person. This could be a teacher at school who you know and trust.

DO: Ask the group to identify someone in their mind as a trusted adult they could go to if they found out someone was self-harming, or if they thought of harming themselves.

God and self-harm

SAY: When it comes to our relationship with God, nothing can stop God loving us – even self-harm. God's word, his Spirit and his Son all reinforce the fact that God deeply loves us.

ASK: Shout out some experiences that we've had or that are in the Bible which explain just how loved we are.

SAY: Sometimes people think that self-harm makes God angry when it doesn't – if anything, it makes him sad to know that we're struggling and we're not sure how to cope in a healthy way.

Go on to explain that God teaches us to love one another and support each other as the Body of Christ. Part of our way of doing that is by supporting those who are struggling and assisting them to receive help. Let's be an example to others of how to talk safely about self-harm and other tough topics and support each other through our struggles.

Depending on your relationship with the group, it may be helpful to explain that, just because you're not studying a particular passage, it doesn't mean that this isn't a valid session. To truly know we are loved by God can utterly transform our lives – including our reactions to emotional distress.

Let us reflect

Ask the group to stand in a circle and explain that those who self-harm are often deeply hurting on the inside, even if sometimes they appear all smiley and OK.

DO: Give everyone a tea-light candle and light the pillar candle in the centre of the circle.

SAY: We all face challenges in our lives and, whether we cope by self-harming or doing something else, we all need support. One way to do this is to pray for one another. Think of one person in your life who needs support. This could be someone in your school or at home. We're going to go around and say a prayer – out loud or in your head – for that person. As you pray, light your tea-light from the 'God' pillar candle and place it next to the pillar candle. After everyone has lit their candle, we will say a final prayer for the group.

End the session by explaining that self-harm doesn't need to be a taboo topic and identify who they can go to if they wish to talk about it further. Encourage the group to think about how they can support one another more as the Body of Christ in this coming week.

Conclusion

Exploring Emotional Health was born out of identifying personally and professionally the need to support youth leaders and adolescents in exploring emotional health and faith.

For many, this book will have helped to begin the much needed conversations around the Christian faith and individuals' mental and emotional health. You are strongly urged not to let it end here, but rather to keep the conversations alive with the young people with whom you work, and seek wisdom on how to move beyond the workshops.

Youth leaders, be encouraged to continue to equip yourselves so you can support young people as best you possibly can; never forgetting to look after your own mental and emotional health.

This is merely the start of an exploratory journey with adolescents, enriching lives, developing stable faith and building generations of resilient young people.

To God be the glory, for ever and ever. Amen.

Appendix

Identifying emotions workshop

Resources Needed
- Whiteboard/flipchart paper
- Pens
- Prizes
- Advice scenarios
- Bibles

Aim:
To understand why feelings are important and to identify the emotions of others and ourselves.

Leader's Notes:
So often when we discuss emotions and feelings there is a negative connotation to it, as if it is a sign of weakness. This is an opportunity to debunk this myth and show how Jesus had emotions too!

Emotional charades

DO: First, ask for a volunteer to be the scribe. Then ask the rest of the group to shout out all the emotions they can think of and ask the scribe to write them down.

Encourage the group to be more creative in their thinking of emotions than just 'happy' and 'sad'. What emotions have they felt this week? Tired? Thankful? Anxious? Hopeful? Guilty? Joyful? Angry? Cheerful? Rejected? Loved? Overwhelmed? Hateful? Daring? Insecure? There are *so* many emotions that we can feel, so get them thinking!

After a good number of emotions have been written down, split the group into two teams. Ask for a volunteer from each team to come to the front. Secretly give them an emotion from the board. They then act it out to their teams, and the first team to guess it correctly wins a point. This can be done for as long as time allows – perhaps even have a prize ready for the winning team!

Jesus' emotions

SAY: Jesus' emotions played a huge feature in his existence on earth. As we study his life, we discover so many scenarios where he experienced a whole heap of feelings – from being a man of sorrows to a man of joy!

ASK: Take a moment to ask the group if they can think of any examples of where Jesus felt and expressed his emotions in the Bible.

Here are some examples that could help this discussion. You could even split them up, asking small groups to discuss and identify the emotions.

Jesus is tested in the wilderness (Matthew 4)

An example here is when Jesus said: 'Away from me, Satan!' (v.10) and the devil left. I doubt Jesus said it in a quiet, timid voice but with a powerful tone, showing just how much he wants and believes in honouring the Lord our God.

The guards mock Jesus (Luke 22:63-65)

When the guards mocked Jesus, how do you think that affected how he felt? Maybe he felt rejected and lonely.

Gethsemane (Mark 14)

When Jesus said: 'My soul is overwhelmed with sorrow to the point of death' (v.34), it is highly unlikely that he was feeling cheerful. How does an overwhelmed soul feel?

SAY: It's important we take note of our feelings rather than ignoring them, as they are a part of who God created us to be. Our emotions can help us grow our sense of self-worth and can help guide us through life.

Emotions are so powerful that they can help us know when to support a friend who's upset, or know when to walk away from an argument. Jesus had feelings; if we are on a quest to become more Christ-like beings, then it's time to learn more about them!

Advice time

By offering advice to others, using our Christ-like nature, the group will be able to look outside themselves and begin to identify emotions of others and subsequently themselves. Feel free to create your own scenarios.

SAY: We all come across various friends and family members who sometimes need advice – including ourselves! Jesus was amazing at giving advice to others and now it's time for us to offer the advice. In pairs/small groups, pick a scenario and discuss the questions at the end. Be ready to explain it to the rest of the group afterwards.

Scenario 1 – Nick and Jamie

For Nick's twelfth birthday his parents took him and a friend to Marwell zoo for the day. He was looking forward to seeing the penguins because they were his favourite! Nick's friend, Jamie, wanted to spend most of his time at the monkey enclosure. The weather changed and the heavy rain meant they all had to go inside. They waited for the rain to stop but it didn't, so Nick's parents decided to take them all home early, without seeing the penguins.

- How do you think Nick might have felt throughout the day?

- Did his feelings change as the day went on? If so, how?

- How do you think Jamie might have felt?

- Did his feelings change throughout the day? If so, how?

- Looking back, how do you think Nick will remember his birthday celebration?

Scenario 2 – Sarah and Gemma

Sarah and Gemma took the bus into town to go shopping. Their parents gave each of them money to pay for the bus tickets. On the way into town, Gemma paid for both of their bus tickets. After they had finished shopping, they decided to get the bus back home. However, Sarah had spent all of the money she took with her, including the bus ticket money from her parents. They were stuck in town alone.

- How do you think Sarah might have felt throughout the day?
- Did her feelings change as the day went on? If so, how?
- How do you think Gemma might have felt?
- Did her feelings change throughout the day? If so, how?
- What memories do you think they will have of this shopping trip?

Scenario 3 – Bethany and Sam

Bethany and Sam have been best friends since primary school. For Bethany's birthday, she went to Thorpe Park and took Sam with her. Sam told Bethany he was scared of the rollercoasters but wanted to go on them. Bethany encouraged Sam to go on one, promising that she'd sit next to him. Sam was so thrilled he conquered his fear and they both enjoyed their day.

- How do you think Bethany might have felt throughout the day?
- Did her feelings change as the day went on? If so, how?
- How do you think Sam might have felt?
- Did his feelings change throughout the day? If so, how?
- What memories do you think they will have of Bethany's birthday celebration?

DO: Take some time to ask each pair/group to feedback their thoughts on the scenario(s). Can they relate to any of them? Does anyone have their own real-life scenario to share?

Close

Take a moment to pray for the group, asking our heavenly Father to help us all realise the power of feelings and remember that acknowledging them is a strength and not a weakness. Perhaps ask one of the group members if they would like to pray for you all.

Challenge

SAY: Over the next week I challenge you to try and identify your emotions and see if they match some of the emotions we have explored today. When you're reading your Bible, think 'is there an emotion I can identify here?' and bring it back next week!

Coping with emotions workshop

Resources Needed
- Talking About Emotions playing cards (These can be purchased from youthscape.co.uk/store or you could create your own.)
- Score board
- Pens
- Post-it notes
- Coloured paper
- Print-outs of the Positive Action list
- Writing paper

Aim:
To explore how we cope with our emotions.

Leader's Notes:
It's helpful to use this as a follow-on from the 'Identifying Emotions' workshop but it can work as a standalone session too. Even though the primary aim of the workshop is to explore coping with emotions, it can also be a helpful time to learn more about one another and help unite the youth group. It is designed to be run as different stations that the young people walk around. Each activity has an explanation that can be printed and displayed next to the station.

Introduction
Begin the workshop by gathering the whole group together. Explain that today is all about exploring how we cope with our emotions. It's a chance to learn from others, learn more about ourselves and connect with God. Explain the different stations and you're all set to go!

Station 1: Snap with a twist

This station explores our emotions from different angles – including understanding emotions, coping with emotions, expressing emotions and emotional perspective. Create a score board and offer a prize for the winner! If purchasing the playing cards isn't an option for you, then you can make your own. An alternative could be using a normal pack of playing cards and writing a list of questions/statements that explore emotions. Match the suit, number or colour to the questions, and each time there is a snap read out the related question.

Explanation: Here's a pack of special cards. Your task is to play snap and become the ultimate winner! The twist is, each time you snap, you have to answer the question or statement that is on the card. Whoever wins by having all the cards at the end gets their name written on the score board. There will be a prize for the person who scores the highest! Remember – it is not a race. You must answer the question properly or you could be stripped of your winning title!

Station 2: Healthy vs unhealthy

This station explores how we cope with emotions and whether we think that is a healthy or unhealthy way of managing our feelings. At the end, you should have a selection of suggested healthy and unhealthy post-it notes on each example.

Create two images of people out of coloured paper and write 'sad' and 'angry' above each. Make sure you don't place them too close together and identify one side of each as healthy and one as unhealthy. Have a pile of post-it notes and pens ready for the group to use.

Explanation: Here are two people. One represents us when we are sad and the other when we are angry. Use the post-it notes provided to write down what you do to cope when you feel those emotions. Think of as many ways as possible and write each one down on separate post-it notes. Then, decide if they are healthy or unhealthy ways of coping and stick them on the right side of the person.

For example, when you are angry you could punch a wall. Decide if that is a healthy or unhealthy way to manage your feelings of anger, then stick the post-it note under the correct heading.

Station 3: Take-away techniques

This station offers positive actions that can help us manage different emotions. Create a poster with the following actions and ask the young people to write down three (or more!) actions they could do to help their emotional health. You could even create an a6 card for them to write down the actions and keep in their wallet or pocket.

Explanation: Here's a whole bunch of different positive actions you can do to help manage your emotions. Pick a minimum of three actions and write them down. Keep that note on you to help you remember different actions you can take to develop your emotional health. Many of them are very general but try them, as they might just work for you!

The Positive Actions List

Exercise – It's a great way to release feel-good chemicals in our brain, such as dopamine which helps us feel better. Plus, it's good for our physical health too!

Be kind to others – This can help take the focus off worrying about yourself but also brings joy to others.

Notice the good things in life – It's easier said than done, but sometimes just taking a moment to pause and think of three good things in your life can help lift your mood. Try it!

Talk it out – Sometimes it can be helpful to chat to a friend about what's on your mind and you can feel like the problem isn't as big any more.

Distract yourself – It's important to recognise how you're feeling and take note of that, but sometimes it can be helpful to distract yourself by watching a movie or heading out for a walk listening to music. It can elevate your mood and refresh your mind.

Don't give in to negative thoughts – We all have an internal monologue at times but if you find you're having negative thoughts, look for evidence against them. Are they really true? Or is it because you're having an 'off day' or you're under stressful circumstances that are out of your control? Don't let the negative thoughts win.

Get outside! – Instead of looking outside and seeing grey skies and rain, see it as an opportunity to jump in a puddle or skim stones on the water. Wrapping up and heading out for a walk on a cold day can get the blood circulating and boost your mood. Simply hang out with nature for a while. Fresh air is excellent medicine, plus it's free!

Be open and accept what is going on – It can be really hard to keep fighting life stressors and can leave you feeling exhausted. Sometimes it helps to pause, appreciate the positives in life and be aware of what is happening around you. Acknowledge your thoughts and feelings but don't overly engage with them for a moment, just 'be'.

Practise gratitude – Say thank you to others and show that you're grateful. Appreciate others and remember those positive moments.

Station 4: Prayer

This station is an opportunity to consciously connect with God in several different ways. It's all about helping the young people to recognise that God and emotions do mix – we are to partner with God. Prayer is a Christian practice that many undervalue, yet it can be so useful when it comes to managing our emotions – especially in the heat of the moment!

Explanation: Here's a chance to consciously connect with God. Spend some time thinking about how you cope with your emotions. Do you manage them in a healthy or unhealthy way? Is there a positive action you can do to help your emotions? Do you pray regularly or is it a one-off thing? Use this as a space to be still and reflect on all that you've learnt in this workshop. You could write a prayer letter to God, asking for help in how to handle a particular emotion or situation. It might be helpful to lie down and close your eyes, saying a silent prayer in your head. Perhaps you could gather together with a few friends to pray for one another.

Begin to draw the session to a close by having an open discussion about how their spiritual lives could be affected by their emotional health. Can God help them to manage their emotions? Are there Christian practices such as praying that can help us?

Finish

There is no specific end to this workshop, which can last until everyone has had an opportunity to take part in all the stations. If time allows, you could gather the group together and ask if anyone found any stations particularly helpful and why. Let the young people know who to go to if they wish to discuss anything more and encourage them to use their positive actions in the coming weeks.

Self-esteem workshop

Resources Needed
- Bowl
- Paper cup
- Jug/bottle of water
- Pin

Aim:

To explore the highs and lows of our own self-esteem

Leader's Notes:

The cup and water activity can be a particularly sensitive activity. Be aware of your group and provide a space for them to chat more if they need to.

What is self-esteem?

Begin the workshop by having an informal conversation with the group about the topic of self-esteem.

What does the word 'self-esteem' mean?

What does it look like?

If someone asked you to explain it, what would you say?

Highs and lows

After defining self-esteem, now is the time to identify the highs and lows of self-esteem. Using a whiteboard or wall space, write two headings – 'Highs' and 'Lows'. Give everyone in the group two post-it notes, and ask them to write down one thing that could bring up a person's self-esteem on the first post-it note. Then ask them to write one thing that could bring it down on another post-it note. Stick the post-it notes under the correct heading so everyone can see them. Take a moment to run through the different examples that are on the wall, explaining that they will be useful for the next activity.

Cup and water activity

This is an opportunity to be open and honest as a youth group. It's a chance to find common ground between one another, realising that no one's self-esteem is perfect. This activity can empower everyone in the group to know they can lift their own self-esteem.

1. Ask the group to stand in a circle and explain that the cup represents us (you could draw a face on it if you want!) and the water represents our self-esteem. Fill the cup half way with water, putting it in the bowl in the centre of the circle.

2. Explain that one by one you're going to go into the centre of the circle, saying one thing that brings your self-esteem down. As you say it, use the pin to pierce the cup. As each person pierces the cup, water will begin to slowly drip out (this is why the bowl is useful!). Go round multiple times, encouraging everyone to be honest in their answers.

3. Pause the group when it feels right and explain that each time you pierce a hole in the cup, it's like a bad experience or a negative comment that lowers our self-esteem. This can be seen by the water slowly dripping out. Explain that sometimes we can shrug off that rude comment or that low grade but, over time, it can substantially lower our self-esteem. We can see that as our self-esteem level – or the water level in the cup – goes down, eventually we could end up with no self-esteem.

4. Share with the group that everyone's self-esteem gets lowered at times and this may not be our fault, but we do have the power to 'top up' our self-esteem level. Pick up the jug of water and explain that this time you're going to share one thing that brings your self-esteem up, pouring a little of the 'self-esteem water' into the cup.

5. Close the activity by explaining that everyone's self-esteem levels are different. What brings one person's self-esteem up, may bring another's down. This shows how different everyone is. Perhaps as a result of hearing what brings other people's self-esteem up, you could try their ideas when you're having a rough day. Encourage the group to remember they have the power to lift their self-esteem, and no one can take that away from them.

End on a high

It's important to lift the mood of the group as the atmosphere can become fragile during the activity. It might be helpful to play a quick game to help everyone leave on a positive note. Remind the group of where to go for additional support if they felt that was needed. Challenge everyone to do one thing that lifts their self-esteem this week – or even try something new! Close the session by praying for one another.

Anxiety workshop

Resources Needed
- Large paper and pens
- Large vase of water
- Dissolvable vitamins
- 1 Peter 5:7

Aim:

To learn more about anxiety and take part in a practical response to 'casting our cares'.

Leader's Notes:

We know how real anxiety can be and how much it can affect our lives. We want to support our young people as much as possible, so don't forget to remind them that there is hope and advise them on where to go for additional support.

Human knot!

DO: Have the group stand in a circle facing the middle. Ask them to reach their right arm towards the centre and grab someone else's hand. Make sure no one holds the hand of the person right next to them. Then do the same with the left arm. The group then work together to untangle the human knot they have created. They can go over and under each other's arms and legs but they must NOT break the chain of connected hands in the process. You could even have a few groups race each other!

At the end, explain that sometimes anxiety can be like a knot in our stomach. Sometimes it can untangle quickly and our anxiety is reduced.

Other times it feels like more and more knots are evolving in our stomach, like a bunch of Russian dolls, and anxiety takes over our mind and body. This week we're going to explore this topic and what the Bible says about it.

Umbrella of anxiety

SAY: Anxiety is like an umbrella with lots of different conditions underneath. This could be OCD, social anxiety, panic attacks, and more. Did you know that one in six young people will experience an anxiety condition at some point in their lives? That means that up to five people in your class at school may be living with anxiety! Anxiety is something we ALL face at different points in our lives but when it begins to negatively affect our daily lives – we need to seek help. But first, let's think about what situations could result in us experiencing anxiety.

Real-life experiences

DO: Split the group into pairs and ask them to think of one real-life situation where someone could experience anxiety. This could be right before they take a music exam or when they walk into a room that is already full of people; from being introduced to a step-parent, to handing in a school project you've been working on day and night.

After giving them time to think, go around and share the different situations. Are any of them the same? Does everyone agree or do some get anxious about something that others aren't bothered about? Is there a theme that runs through this group's anxieties that you can pick up on?

Mind, body and soul

DO: Ask for a volunteer and draw around them on a large piece of paper so you have an outline of a human. Ask the group to write on the paper what they think anxiety is like. For example, in the brain you could draw a thought bubble with anxious thoughts like 'I'm nervous about the school play' or 'I'm worried they don't like me.' Where the heart is meant to be, you could draw a heart that is racing away to show an elevated heart rate. Provoke a discussion around their spiritual lives – how does anxiety affect their relationship with God? Encourage the group to get creative!

SAY: Looking at the human we have created, we can see how much anxiety can affect different areas of our lives – from our minds to our bodies to our souls. We can see how different it is for everyone and recognise that it's OK to experience it differently.

Good news!

SAY: The good news is that we can learn to control our anxieties and we don't have to face them alone – hooray! In 1 Peter chapter 5 verse 7, we are reminded to cast our cares on God because God cares for us. These powerful words are so helpful to remember if we are suffering from anxiety.

ASK: Does anyone know what the words 'cast your cares' means?

SAY: Casting our cares is offering our anxieties to God. Its action is us praying to God and giving our anxieties to him, trusting that he will take care of the situation. We can cast our cares on God because he cares for us – it's an amazing feeling to know that our loving Father cares for us. He loves us so much that he wants our anxieties to become more manageable. He cares for each and every one of us – no matter how anxious we get!

ASK: Is it easy to cast our cares on God? Does it come naturally to you? Do you believe God cares for us?

Vitamins and water

SAY: Imagine these tablets are like our anxieties (give examples of ones that have been discussed through the session). Each time you offer your anxieties to God, it's like dropping a tablet in the water – the anxiety is diluted in God's hand. The cause of the anxiety may not disappear, but the effect on us is less concentrated.

DO: Standing in a circle, ask the group to take a tablet in their hand and silently think of an anxiety they are experiencing. Ask them to take turns to put the tablet in the water as a symbol of casting that anxiety on God, remembering he cares for us. Repeat this as necessary.

Pray
Ask the group to put their right hand on the right shoulder of the person standing on their right-hand side. Then, encourage the young people to pray for the person their hand is touching to know that they can cast their cares on God because he cares for them.

Challenge
As a way of moving forward, challenge the group to think – what one anxiety do you have that you could begin to face this week knowing that God cares for you? Report back to us next session.

Depression workshop

Resources Needed
- Bibles/print-outs of Matthew 26:37-39
- Print-outs of 'Depression is like . . .'

Aim:
To be a starting point for gaining a basic understanding of depression, and how Jesus brings us all hope.

Leader's Notes:
It's important that you offer support for those who may need it after the session has ended. Everyone is susceptible to experiencing bouts of depression, but for some it is an illness that requires further intervention. Be sure to know your safeguarding policy in case you need to take action. Remember, talking about depression doesn't have to be a solemn experience – embrace the laughter of games and the joy Jesus brings!

Introduction
SAY: Depression is a huge topic! It's one word that has so much linked to it and we're going to start discovering that today. A helpful definition of depression is from the World Health Organisation which says, *'Depression is a common mental disorder, characterised by sadness, loss of interest or pleasure, feelings of guilt or low self-worth, disturbed sleep or appetite, feelings of tiredness, and poor concentration.'*

Continue to explain to the group that depression appears in both the Old and New Testaments and people are experiencing it this very day. It's real and it's time to start getting clued up about it.

True or false?

DO: Identify one end of the room as true and the other end as false. Read out the following statements – or create more of your own – and ask the group to run to the side they think is correct, and then re-centre the group after each statement is read. You could even ask one of the group members to be the 'quiz master'!

1. You can snap out of depression just by thinking positively.
   FALSE: Depression is a serious illness. Many never seek treatment but people can get better with the right support.

2. The best way to help someone who is depressed is to try and cheer them up.
   FALSE: The best way to help someone is to encourage them to seek out help by speaking to a person they trust and heading to their GP.

3. Christians can't suffer from depression.
   FALSE: Christians can suffer from depression, just as they can suffer from the flu or any other illness.

4. One in ten children and young people are affected by a mental health problem.
   TRUE: That's around three students in every class!

5. No one in the Bible suffered from depression or depressive symptoms.
   FALSE: A whole heap of people did – Elijah, Job, Moses, Jonah, Jeremiah and even Jesus!

Gather the group together at the end and ask if anyone knew the answers already. Have a mini-discussion at this point about what they do and don't already know about depression.

Depression is like . . .

SAY: Talking about our emotional health can be difficult at times, especially when it comes to explaining what it feels like.

DO: Lay out the following verses face-down and ask each person to pick one up and read it out in turn. Use this time to discuss any reflections the group has on these descriptions of what depression is like.

1. My guilt has overwhelmed me like a burden too heavy to bear. *Psalm 38:4*

2. Why, my soul, are you downcast? Why so disturbed within me? *Psalm 42:11*

3. [Elijah] came to a broom bush, sat down under it and prayed that he might die. 'I have had enough, Lord,' he said. 'Take my life; I am no better than my ancestors.' *1 Kings 19:4*

4. 'Now, Lord, take away my life, for it is better for me to die than to live.' *Jonah 4:3*

5. 'My soul is overwhelmed with sorrow to the point of death.' *Matthew 26:38*

Jesus' strategy

SAY: As we look through the Bible at Jesus' life we can see that he also suffered from bouts of depression – just as you and I might do in our lives. We also know that Jesus brings us all hope! If we delve into Matthew's account in chapter 26, we can see how Jesus brings hope to depression. If we look closely, he demonstrates a strategy in Gethsemane of what to do when a bout of depression begins to take over, as a way of confronting and overcoming the overwhelming circumstances he faces.

DO: Ask a volunteer to read Matthew 26:37-39. You could even ask them to read it out like a monologue.

ASK: In pairs/small groups, ask them if they can identify the strategy Jesus uses.

Explain the strategy: There is no set way this needs to be done, so feel free to be as creative as you like, making sure it is clear. You could write each point down and make a flow chart out of them and ask the young people to annotate it – the possibilities are endless!

1. He chose close friends to be with at this difficult time (v.37)

2. He opened his soul to them, telling them how he felt (v.38)

3. He asked them to be with him (v.38)

4. He poured his heart out to the Father (v.39)

5. He rested his soul in God by trusting in his will (v.39)

Provoke a discussion around their thoughts and opinions of the strategy. Is it something they could do? How could the strategy look for them? Can they identify the close friends they could open their soul up to? What could it look like for them to rest their soul in God by trusting his will? Can they provide examples? The strategy can be used by anyone as a tool to help our emotional wellbeing.

Hope

Move your conversation on to focus on the hope we have as Christians. Explain that Jesus repeatedly prayed that God's will be done, *despite* how overwhelmed and hopeless he was feeling (v. 39, v. 42, v. 43). Take a moment to unpack this with the group. What do they think about this? Is this something they can relate to? Can they have hope in their own lives?

Prayers of hope

Move your conversations on from inwardly thinking how Jesus brings hope to ourselves and think of the wider world. Explain that Jesus brings hope to our friends and family, to countries and nations – his hope is for everyone and that is glorious!

Ask everyone to find a space in the room to sit and pause, closing their eyes if that's helpful. Take a moment of silence to reflect on the busy session. Encourage them to pray for the wider world; for people persecuted for being Christians, for war-torn countries and the refugees fleeing their homes for safety; and for those feeling hopeless to become hopeful.

End note
Don't forget to remind young people of where they can go if they need extra support from this session.

Self-harm workshop

Resources Needed
- Post-it notes
- Pens
- Print-out of fact and myth statements
- Pillar candle
- Tea lights
- Lighter
- Taboo cards

Aim:

To explore the topic of self-harm in a safe space and to support one another.

Leader's Notes:

Talking about self-harm can be challenging but please don't ignore this topic. Young people are smart and many of them are aware of self-harm to some degree. Use this as an opportunity to educate them, demonstrating that it's OK to talk about it. Please note that leading a session on self-harm can be emotionally exhausting, so remember to look after yourself. Self-harm doesn't have to be a taboo topic, but it does require self-awareness in order to support others effectively.

TABOO!

DO: This classic card game is all about guessing the word being described, without using any of the Taboo words listed on the card. One person selects a card to describe and the rest of the team have to guess. The more creative the clues, the better!

If you don't already have the card game, don't panic! There are many free printable copies which are easily found online; simply type 'taboo printable cards' in Google and there will be lots to choose from.

SAY: That game was all about taboo words and there are some words and topics we just don't talk about. Self-harm can be one of them, but today we're going to discuss it!

So, what is self-harm?

DO: Ask the young people to take a post-it note and answer the question: 'What is self-harm?' Take all the post-it notes in and give them a quick read so you can gauge how much the group knows.

SAY: The word 'self-harm' covers a few different areas.

- It can be <u>physical</u>, also known as 'self-injury', which is to deliberately harm/injure yourself (hair pulling, cutting, burning).

- It can be <u>behavioural</u>, also known as 'harming behaviours', that have a long-term health effect, like binge drinking or risky sexual behaviour.

- It's not always physical harm but can be <u>emotionally</u> harming ourselves, like judging ourselves really harshly or constantly putting ourselves down to a point where it affects our day-to-day lives.

Myth or fact?

SAY: There are a whole bunch of things being said about self-harm and the individuals who take part in it. It's all over the news and perhaps even in discussions in your schools. Now's the time to get our facts straight and bust myths around this topic!

DO: Split the group into teams, giving them a set of statements. Working together, ask the teams to make two piles of myths and facts, putting each statement in the pile they think is correct. When the teams have finished, go through the statements one at a time and ask them to explain why they've put it in the myths or facts pile. Afterwards, explain the correct answer. Use this as a time to openly discuss self-harm in a safe environment.

STATEMENT 1 – Only teenagers self-harm

MYTH: People of all ages can self-harm. It seems more common in teenagers as this is the age when people tend to begin self-harming and tell someone about it.

STATEMENT 2 – People self-harm because 'it feels nice'

MYTH: Self-harm is anything but nice. Often, people do it as a release of emotional pain they feel inside. Many people feel a rush of adrenalin before they harm, but then they feel the pain after that numbness has left.

STATEMENT 3 – You can get help if you self-harm

FACT: Everyone can get help. There are loads of people who can support you, including family, friends and health professionals. Self-harming is not an end point, but an opportunity to seek help and recover.

STATEMENT 4 – People self-harm just for attention

MYTH: It's really damaging to call someone an attention seeker. It's belittling their problem and saying they don't deserve help. We all need help and support at different times in our lives and sometimes this is a way of saying 'I need help'.

STATEMENT 5 – Self-harm is a suicide attempt

MYTH: Self-harm is very much a way of coping with life. By self-harming, people can feel they're being helped to get through day-to-day life.

SAY: There is so much information around self-harm and people have many assumptions about why a person is self-harming. We can use the information we've learnt from these myths and facts to help ourselves and others around this topic.

What to do if you think someone is self-harming

DO: Ask the group to turn to the person next to them and think about what they would do if they thought someone they knew was self-harming. Ask volunteers to share their thoughts.

SAY: If you know someone is self-harming or has said to you that they are thinking of harming themselves, it's really important that you tell a trusted adult. They can then go on to help that person. This could be a teacher at school who you know and trust.

DO: Ask the group to identify someone in their mind as a trusted adult they could go to if they found out someone was self-harming, or if they thought of harming themselves.

God and self-harm

SAY: When it comes to our relationship with God, nothing can stop God loving us – even self-harm. God's word, his Spirit and his Son all reinforce the fact that God deeply loves us.

ASK: Shout out some experiences that we've had or that are in the Bible which explain just how loved we are.

SAY: Sometimes people think that self-harm makes God angry when it doesn't – if anything, it makes him sad to know that we're struggling and we're not sure how to cope in a healthy way.

Go on to explain that God teaches us to love one another and support each other as the Body of Christ. Part of our way of doing that is by supporting those who are struggling and assisting them to receive help. Let's be an example to others of how to talk safely about self-harm and other tough topics and support each other through our struggles.

Let us reflect

Ask the group to stand in a circle and explain that those who self-harm are often deeply hurting on the inside, even if sometimes they appear all smiley and OK.

DO: Give everyone a tea-light candle and light the pillar candle in the centre of the circle.

SAY: We all face challenges in our lives and, whether we cope by self-harming or doing something else, we all need support. One way to do this is to pray for one another. Think of one person in your life who needs support. This could be someone in your school or at home. We're going to go around and say a prayer – out loud or in your head – for that person. As you pray, light your tea-light from the 'God' pillar candle and place it next to the pillar candle. After everyone has lit their candle, we will say a final prayer for the group.

End the session by explaining that self-harm doesn't need to be a taboo topic and identify who they can go to if they wish to talk about it further. Encourage the group to think about how they can support one another more as the Body of Christ in this coming week.

Further Reading

Books

Goleman, D. (1996), *Emotional Intelligence*, London: Bloomsbury.

Middleton, K. (2008), *Self Harm: The Path to Recovery*, Oxford: Lion Hudson.

Steiner, C. (2003), *Emotional Literacy: Intelligence with a Heart*, California: Personhood Press.

Thomson, J. (2016), *Relationships and Emotions after Christendom*, Milton Keynes: Paternoster.

Report papers

Department of Health (2015), *Future in Mind*. Available at: < https://www.gov.uk/government/uploads/system/uploads/attachment_data/file/414024/Childrens_Mental_Health.pdf> [Accessed: 10 February 2017]

Girlguiding (2016), *Girls' Attitude Survey*. Available at: < https://www.girlguiding.org.uk/social-action-advocacy-and-campaigns/research/girls-attitudes-survey/> [Accessed: 10 February 2017]

Mental Health Foundation (2006), *The impact of spirituality on mental health*. Available at: < https://www.mentalhealth.org.uk/publications/impact-spirituality-mental-health> [Accessed 10 February 2017]

Mental Health Foundation (2015), *Fundamental Facts about Mental Health*. Available at: < https://www.mentalhealth.org.uk/publications/fundamental-facts-about-mental-health-2015>